HUMAN PHYSIOLOGICAL ANATOMY
LABORATORY MANUAL

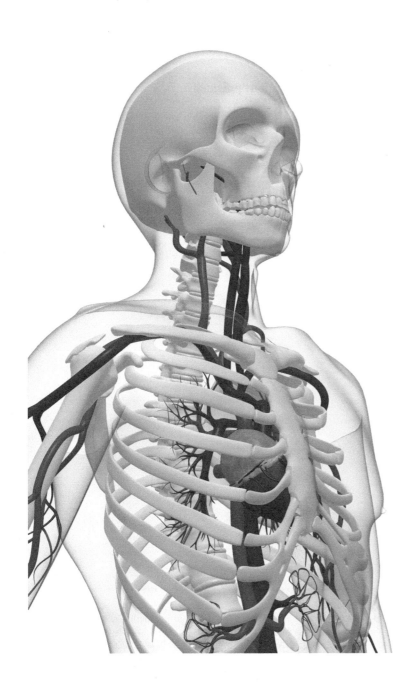

Wanda F. Ragland

Macomb Community College

macmillan learning
curriculum solutions

Sustainability
Hayden-McNeil's standard paper stock uses a minimum of 30% post-consumer waste. We offer higher % options by request, including a 100% recycled stock. Additionally, Hayden-McNeil Custom Digital provides authors with the opportunity to convert print products to a digital format. Hayden-McNeil is part of a larger sustainability initiative through Macmillan Learning. Visit http://sustainability.macmillan.com to learn more.

bedford/st. martin's • hayden-mcneil
w.h. freeman • worth publishers

TABLE OF CONTENTS

UNIT 1 FUNDAMENTALS, INTEGUMENT, SKELETON, AND MUSCLES   1

Part 1: Introduction and Fundamentals 1

Part 2: The Integument 9

Part 3: The Skeleton 11

    Section A: Bone Tissue and Long Bone Structure 11

    Section B: Appendicular Skeleton—Upper Limb 14

    Section C: Appendicular Skeleton—Lower Limb 20

    Section D: Axial Skeleton—Vertebral Column 25

    Section E: Axial Skeleton—Rib Cage 30

    Section F: Axial Skeleton—Skull 31

Part 4: Muscles 41

    Section A: Muscle Tissue 41

    Section B: Muscles of the Face and Neck 43

    Section C: Muscles of the Trunk 45

    Section D: Muscles of the Upper Limb 51

    Section E: Muscles of the Pelvis, Buttocks, and Lower Limb 53

UNIT 2 NERVOUS TISSUE, CENTRAL NERVOUS SYSTEM, SPECIAL SENSES, AND ENDOCRINE SYSTEM   63

Part 1: Nervous Tissue and the Neuron 63

Part 2: The Brain 68

Part 3: The Spinal Cord, Somatic Reflex Arc, Visceral Reflex Arc 81

Part 4: Special Senses 87

    Section A: The Ear 87

    Section B: The Eye 91

Part 5: The Endocrine System 94

UNIT 3   BLOOD, CARDIOVASCULAR SYSTEM, LYMPHATICS, RESPIRATORY SYSTEM   105

Part 1: Blood 105

    Section A: Formed Elements 105

    Section B: Laboratory Tests 108

    Section C: Blood Types 110

Part 2: Heart 113

    Section A: External Anatomy of the Heart 113

    Section B: Internal Anatomy of the Heart 116

    Section C: Dissection of the Sheep Heart 120

Part 3: Blood Vessels 127

    Section A: Blood Vessels 127

    Section B: Systemic Arteries 128

    Section C: Systemic Veins 136

    Section D: Hepatic Portal System 139

    Section E: Blood Pressure 140

Part 4: Lymphatics 141

Part 5: Respiratory System 143

    Section A: Anatomy of the Respiratory System 143

    Section B: Pulmonary Volumes 151

UNIT 4   DIGESTIVE SYSTEM, URINARY SYSTEM, REPRODUCTIVE SYSTEMS   153

Part 1: Digestive Tract 153

Part 2: Urinary System 162

Part 3: Female Reproductive System 168

Part 4: Male Reproductive System 171

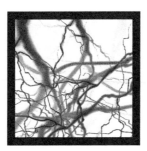

INTRODUCTION

Welcome to Human Physiological Anatomy. This course is designed for students in the Health and Human Services programs. It is an intensive lecture/laboratory course emphasizing the basic concepts and principles of human anatomy and physiology. The purpose of this manual is to assist the student in meeting the laboratory objectives for this course. The laboratory objectives can be found in the course objective handbook available in the bookstore.

This manual is divided into four units that correspond to the four lab practical exams in this course. Your laboratory objectives identify the structures that you are responsible for on each lab practical. You should cross-reference the objectives with the information in each unit of this manual.

This laboratory manual should be used as a guide to help you study the models, charts, and dissected organs in the lab. It is only meant to guide you in your studies.

Each structure in the figures is identified by a number or letter. There is a key for each figure that matches the number or letter to the structure. This design was chosen to allow you to cover the key and test yourself on each figure.

STUDENT CODE OF CONDUCT

Students are expected to behave in the following manner in the anatomy lab:

- Students must behave in a mature and responsible manner at all times in the laboratory. All inappropriate behavior is prohibited.

- Students must report any injuries or breakages to the instructor immediately.

- At no time will biological tissue or anatomical models be removed from the laboratory.

- At no time will food or drink be permitted in the laboratory.

- All cell phones and/or pagers must be turned off in the laboratory.

- Using a pen or pencil to point out structures on a model or a chart is strictly prohibited. Writing or circling structures on any charts is strictly prohibited.

- Students must return models to tables if moved during the laboratory session.

- Any keys to models or charts must not be removed from the laboratory. If a student would like a copy of any key, he/she may request one from the instructor.

- All biological tissue will be placed in the appropriate biological waste receptacle. At no time will any other material (e.g., paper products) be placed in this receptacle.

- Students are responsible for cleaning their table after dissections. Students must clean their instruments and dissecting pans. All equipment must be returned to the appropriate area in the laboratory.

- All paper and disposable gloves must be disposed of in the metal trash containers. Do not place paper in the biological tissue containers. Do not use the table sinks as trash receptacles.

- Women who are pregnant or who may become pregnant should discuss the potential risk of dissection and exposure to preservatives with their obstetrician. Material safety data sheets (MSDS) are available.

- Models or displays must not be removed from any practice lab practical. Models from the tables should not be moved and placed into the practice lab practical setup.

- During lab practical exams, students must not touch the models or displays.

I have read and understood the Student Code of Conduct

_____

Student Signature   *Date*   *Section*

UNIT 1

FUNDAMENTALS, INTEGUMENT, SKELETON, AND MUSCLES

PART 1

INTRODUCTION AND FUNDAMENTALS

To be successful in any field or discipline it is necessary to speak the language. Before learning about tissues, organs and organ systems, it is necessary to learn the correct terminology to adequately describe the structures you will be learning. Trying to discuss anatomy without understanding anatomical terms would be impossible. As you enter the medical field you need to convey information accurately and precisely in terms everyone else in the field can understand.

There are specific terms used to describe direction, parts of the body, cavities of the body, and areas within the cavities. The next sections will help you develop your terminology so you can begin to "talk the talk."

DIRECTIONAL TERMS

Directional terms are used to accurately describe the location of a structure or organ. The terms used to describe anatomical directions can usually be paired as opposites.

These directional terms are only meaningful if they are applied consistently. In order to have the terms used the same way by everyone they must be used when the body is in a specific position. This is known as **anatomical position**. Anatomical position is an individual facing forward, feet facing forward, arms at side with palms facing forward.

Table 1.1: Directional Terms

TERM	DEFINITION	EXAMPLE
Anterior	The front, in front of (equivalent to ventral)	The stomach is anterior to the kidney
Distal	Away from or farthest from the point of attachment or origin	The wrist is distal to the shoulder
Dorsal	The back, behind (equivalent to posterior)	The dorsal root ganglion
Inferior	Below or towards the feet	The liver is inferior to the diaphragm
Lateral	At or towards the side	The lungs are lateral to the heart
Medial	Towards the body's midline	The heart is medial to the lungs
Posterior	The back or behind (equivalent to dorsal)	The kidneys are posterior to the liver
Proximal	Towards or closest to the point of attachment or origin	The elbow is proximal to the wrist
Superior	Above or toward the head	The lungs are superior to the diaphragm
Ventral	The abdominal side, in humans the front (equivalent to anterior)	The ventral nerve roots

BODY PLANES

There are ways to dissect the body in order to observe all structures and organs from different aspects. A body or structure can be dissected to divide it into right and left sides. This is a **sagittal** (SAJ-it-ahl) section. If the division is directly in the midline it may be referred to as a **midsagittal** section. It is possible to dissect a body or a structure to divide it into front and back sections. This is a **frontal** section. The last plane that can be used to divide a body or a structure is to dissect it into top and bottom portions. This is a **transverse** section.

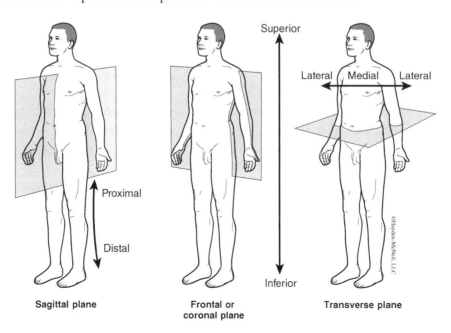

Figure 1.1. Planes of the Body

REGIONAL TERMS

Terms that refer to different regions of the body will help you understand where to find structures and organs.

Table 1.2: Regional Terms

TERM	LOCATION	TERM	LOCATION
Abdominal	Abdomen	Gluteal	Buttocks
Antebrachial	Forearm	Inguinal	Groin
Antecubital	Anterior elbow	Lumbar	Lower back
Axillary	Armpit	Palmar	Palm of hand
Brachial	Arm	Patellar	Anterior knee
Buccal	Cheek	Pectoral	Chest
Carpal	Wrist	Pedal	Foot
Caudal	Lower body	Pelvic	Pelvis
Cephalic	Head	Plantar	Sole of foot
Cervical	Neck	Popliteal	Posterior knee
Costal	Ribs	Tarsal	Ankle
Cubital	Posterior elbow	Thoracic	Chest
Femoral	Thigh	Visceral	Organ or viscera

ABDOMINAL REGIONS

To try and localize areas in the abdomen the abdominal region can be divided into 4 quadrants or 9 regions. The quadrants are referred to as right and left and upper and lower. The four quadrants would be: right upper quadrant, right lower quadrant, left upper quadrant, and left lower quadrant.

The nine regions can be defined by drawing 2 horizontal lines about halfway between the midline and the side of the body and 2 vertical lines, one near the bottom of the ribs and the second near the top of the ribs. The regions down the center of the abdomen have unique names: epigastric (top center region); umbilical (middle center region); and hypogastric (lower center region). The regions on either side of the abdomen have the same names that are differentiated as right and left. These regions are the right and left hypochondriac regions, just below the ribs; the right and left lumbar regions, on either side of the umbilical region; and the right and left iliac or inguinal regions, at the lower boundary of the abdomen. Table 1.3 identifies the regions and the organs or structures that can be found in each region.

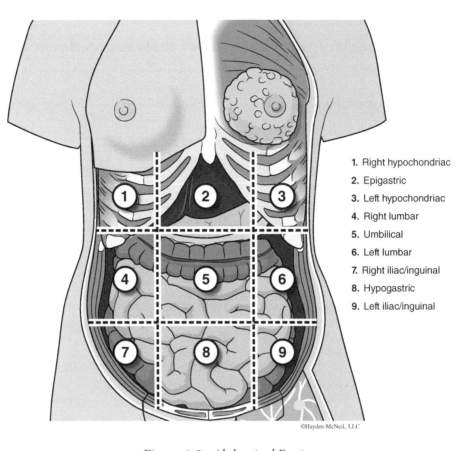

1. Right hypochondriac
2. Epigastric
3. Left hypochondriac
4. Right lumbar
5. Umbilical
6. Left lumbar
7. Right iliac/inguinal
8. Hypogastric
9. Left iliac/inguinal

©Hayden-McNeil, LLC

Figure 1.2. Abdominal Regions

Table 1.3: Regions and Their Structures

RIGHT HYPOCHONDRIAC (1)	EPIGASTRIC (2)	LEFT HYPOCHONDRIAC (3)
Right lobe of liver	Pyloric end of stomach	Stomach
Gallbladder	Duodenum/Left lobe of liver	Spleen
Right adrenal gland	Pancreas	Left adrenal gland
RIGHT LUMBAR (4)	**UMBILICAL (5)**	**LEFT LUMBAR (6)**
Ascending colon	Omentum	Descending colon
Right kidney	Mesentery	Left kidney
Portion of small intestine	Small intestine	Portion of small intestine
RIGHT ILIAC/INGUINAL (7)	**HYPOGASTRIC (8)**	**LEFT ILIAC/INGUINAL (9)**
Cecum of large intestines	Ileum	Sigmoid colon
Appendix	Bladder	Left ureter
Right ovary	Uterus	Left ovary

BODY CAVITIES

All the internal body organs, also known as the **viscera** (VIS-er-ah), are located in cavities. These cavities are usually lined with membranes. There are 2 major cavities: the **dorsal cavity**, which contains the cranial and spinal cavities; and the **ventral cavity**, which contains the **thoracic** (tho-RAS-ik) and **abdominopelvic** (ab-DOM-eh-no-PEL-vik) cavities.

The **cranial cavity** contains the brain and the **spinal cavity** contains the spinal cord. Both of these structures are covered by three membranes known as the meninges.

The **thoracic cavity**, commonly referred to as the chest cavity, is found in the anterior portion of the body. This cavity is in the ventral cavity superior to the diaphragm. The main structures in the thoracic cavity are the lungs and the heart.

Each lung is covered by a double membrane known as the **pleura** (PLOO-ra). The pleura that is closest to the lung is the **visceral** (VIS-er-ahl) **pleura**, while the pleura that lines the rib cage is the **parietal** (pah-RYE-ah-tahl) **pleura** and the fluid-filled virtual space between them is the **pleural cavity**. So each lung is in the pleural cavity within the thoracic cavity.

The heart is found between the two lungs in the area known as the **mediastinum** (me-de-ah-STY-num). The heart sits inside a sac called the fibrous pericardium. Lining this sac is a double membrane called the serous pericardium. The membrane closest to the heart is the **visceral pericardium** (PER-eh-KARD-eum), while the membrane lining the pericardial sac is the **parietal pericardium**. As with the lungs the fluid-filled virtual space between the two pericardial membranes is the **pericardial cavity**.

The abdominopelvic cavity is the portion of the ventral cavity that is inferior to the diaphragm. It can be further subdivided into the upper portion, the abdominal cavity, and the lower portion, the pelvic cavity. The abdominal cavity extends from the diaphragm to the area of the bony pelvis. The pelvic cavity is enclosed by the pelvic bones or the **os coxae** (OS COX-ee). The abdominal cavity contains the liver, stomach, spleen, pancreas, gallbladder, and small and large intestines. The pelvic cavity contains the urinary bladder, the sigmoid colon, rectum, and reproductive organs. The double membrane that covers most but not all the organs in the abdominopelvic cavity is the **peritoneum** (per-eh-toe-NEE-um). Just like in the thoracic cavity the membrane closest to the organs is the **visceral peritoneum**, the membrane closer to the abdominal wall is the **parietal peritoneum**, and the virtual space between them is the **peritoneal cavity**. There are abdominal organs that are not covered by the peritoneum. They are located near the posterior wall of the abdominal cavity. The most notable organs are the kidneys. The area containing organs not covered by the peritoneum is the **retroperitoneal space** (RET-row-per-eh-toe-NEE-al).

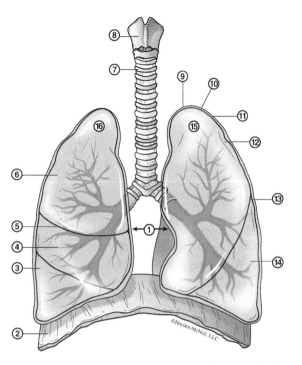

1. Mediastinum
2. Diaphragm
3. Right lower lobe
4. Right middle lobe
5. Horizontal fissure
6. Right upper lobe
7. Trachea
8. Larynx
9. Parietal pleura
10. Visceral pleura
11. Pleural cavity
12. Left upper lobe
13. Oblique fissure
14. Left inferior lobe
15. Left lung
16. Right lung

Figure 1.3. Frontal View of Thorax

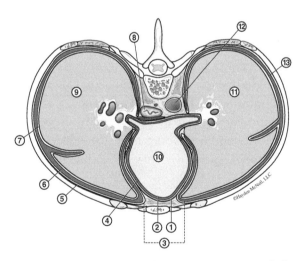

1. Parietal pericardium
2. Visceral pericardium
3. Mediastinum
4. Pericardial cavity
5. Parietal pleura
6. Right pleural cavity
7. Visceral pleura
8. Esophagus
9. Right lung
10. Heart
11. Left lung
12. Descending aorta
13. Left pleural cavity

Figure 1.4. Transverse View of Thorax

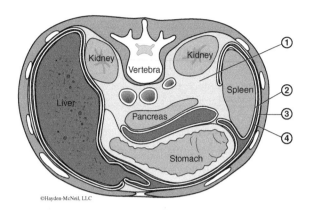

1. Retroperitoneal space
2. Visceral peritoneum
3. Parietal peritoneum
4. Peritoneal cavity

Figure 1.5. Transverse View of Abdomen

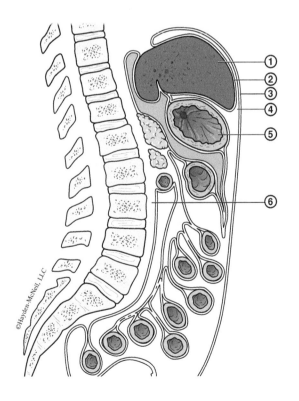

1. Liver
2. Visceral peritoneum
3. Parietal peritoneum
4. Peritoneal cavity
5. Stomach
6. Retroperitoneal space

Figure 1.6. Sagittal View of Abdomen

7

TRANSPORT MECHANISMS

Cells must have an ability to move materials in and out through the plasma membrane. Depending on the nature and size of the materials they may move passively by diffusion or osmosis.

DIFFUSION

Diffusion is the movement of materials from an area of high concentration to an area of low concentration. Diffusion does not require a cell membrane, it can occur in any medium. You can observe diffusion by adding a dye, methylene blue, to a container of water. Gradually the blue color will disperse through the whole container.

Another way to observe diffusion over a much longer period of time is to use a denser medium than water. Adding methylene blue to a test tube of gel will allow you to observe diffusion over a period of weeks. The gel is thicker than water so it will take much longer for the color to disperse.

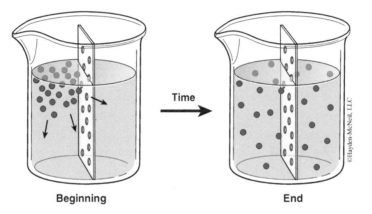

Time

Beginning   **End**

Figure 1.7. Process of Diffusion

OSMOSIS

Osmosis is a special type of diffusion. Osmosis is the diffusion of water through a selectively permeable membrane from an area of high concentration of water, low concentration of solute to an area of low concentration of water, high concentration of solute. The solute cannot move through the membrane. This can result in a change of volume of the cell.

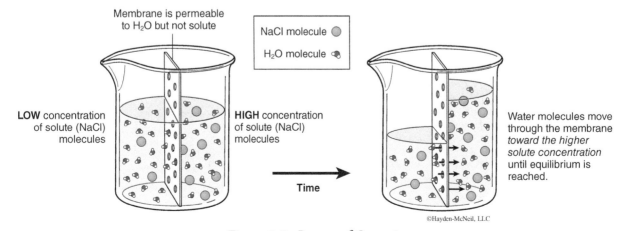

Membrane is permeable to H_2O but not solute

NaCl molecule ⬤
H_2O molecule

LOW concentration of solute (NaCl) molecules

HIGH concentration of solute (NaCl) molecules

Water molecules move through the membrane *toward the higher solute concentration* until equilibrium is reached.

Time

©Hayden-McNeil, LLC

Figure 1.8. Process of Osmosis

The principle of osmosis can be observed using a thistle tube setup. A solution with a high concentration of sugar and low concentration of water is placed in the thistle tube and a selectively permeable membrane is placed across the bottom of the thistle tube. When the thistle tube is lowered into a container that contains water, water will move from the beaker (higher concentration of water) into the thistle tube (lower concentration of water). You will be able to observe this water movement by watching the upward movement of the solution in the thistle tube. The force that causes the increase in the solution volume in the thistle tube is osmotic pressure.

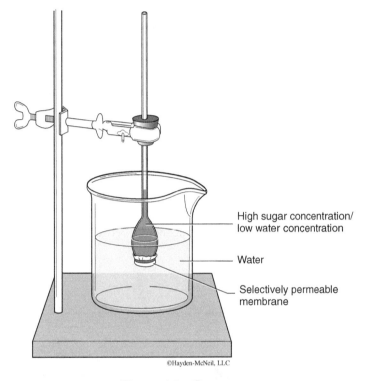

High sugar concentration/
low water concentration

Water

Selectively permeable
membrane

©Hayden-McNeil, LLC

Figure 1.9. Osmometer

PART 2

THE INTEGUMENT

The **integument** (in-TEG-you-ment) is the skin. This is an important organ. It is the body's first line of defense. The skin consists of two distinct tissue layers. The superficial layer, the epidermis, consists of many thin layers of epithelial tissue, and the deeper layer, the dermis, is connective tissue.

The epidermis reproduces cells at the bottom layer and the cells move upward. As the cells progress through the layers of the epidermis they change and eventually die as they reach the surface. At this point they are shed.

The dermis is frequently referred to as the "true skin." In the dermis are all the structures that are frequently associated with skin. Structures found in the dermal layer include: hair follicles, sweat and sebaceous glands, blood vessels, and nervous tissue to name a few.

At the junction of the epidermis and dermis there are fingerlike projections: the dermal **papillae** (pah-PIL-ah). These papillae are responsible for ridges that are visible on the fingertips, palms, and soles. The patterns of the ridges are responsible for your fingerprints, palm prints, and footprints. They can be used for identification because the pattern is unique in each individual. However, the function is not identification. Dermal papillae function in grip. These ridges allow our hands and feet to grip surfaces and items.

The hair follicle consists of epidermal tissue that extends down into the dermis. Associated with the hair follicle is the arrector **pili** (PIE-lie) or (PILL-ee) muscle. When this muscle contracts it causes the hair to stand more upright and results in "goose pimples." Frequently associated with the hair follicles are the **sebaceous** (sah-BAY-shus) glands. These glands produce **sebum** (SEE-bum), an oily secretion that helps keep the hair and skin pliable and contributes to the waterproof nature of the skin. In some areas sebaceous glands may open directly to the skin.

Sweat or **sudoriferous** (sood-ah-RIF-ah-rahus) glands are found in the dermis. There are two types of sweat glands. **Eccrine** (EK-rahn) or (EK-ryne) sweat glands are found all over the body and respond to changes in body temperature. As the sweat evaporates from the skin the body is cooled. Eccrine sweat glands are active throughout life. **Apocrine** (AP-ah-crahn) or (AP-ah-cryne) sweat glands are only found in select sites in the body and become active at puberty. The secretion of these sweat glands is metabolized by skin bacteria.

Several different types of receptors are also present in the dermis. These receptors take many forms and are responsible for monitoring temperature, pressure, vibration, touch, pain, and other sensory input.

The layer below the dermis is known as the hypodermis or subcutaneous layer. This layer serves to attach the skin to the underlying structures. In the subcutaneous layer there are major blood vessels that supply the skin and adipose tissue, which provides the body with insulation. There is not a distinct border between the dermis and the subcutaneous layer.

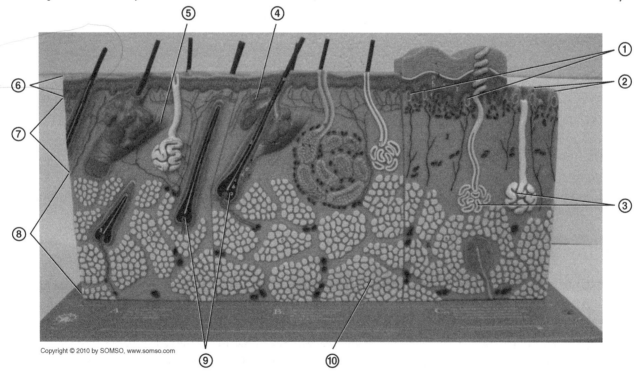

Copyright © 2010 by SOMSO, www.somso.com

1. Receptors (nervous tissue)
2. Dermal papillae
3. Sweat (sudoriferous) glands
4. Sebaceous gland
5. Arrector pili muscle
6. Epidermis
7. Dermis
8. Hypodermis (subcutaneous tissue)
9. Hair follicles
10. Adipose tissue

Figure 1.10. Skin Model

PART 3

THE SKELETON

This section will look at bone tissue, the structure of the long bone, and the skeleton. It is necessary to be able to identify the bones and their markings before moving on to the muscles. Since muscle names may include bones or markings it is helpful in identifying the muscle if a student is familiar with the skeleton first.

SECTION A – BONE TISSUE AND LONG BONE STRUCTURE

Bone Tissue

Bone is a connective tissue, which means it contains matrix. Matrix is the extracellular material in the tissue. There are two types of bone based on structure: compact bone and **cancellous** (KAN-silahs) or spongy bone.

Compact bone is found on the surface of all bones and is the bone tissue in the shafts of long bone. It has a very regular pattern of **osteons** (os-TEE-on), the fundamental unit of compact bone. The structures of the osteon include the central or osteonic canal, lamellae, osteocytes, lacuna, canaliculi, and perforating canals.

The **central** or **osteonic canal** contains blood vessels and lymphatics. The **lamellae** (lah-MEL-ah) are the concentric rings of matrix. The **osteocytes** (OS-te-o-sites) are bone cells sitting in **lacunae** (lah-KU-nah), which are depressions in the matrix. The osteocytes are responsible for maintaining the matrix. The **canaliculi** (KAN-AHLIK-yahlie) are small channels that allow extensions of the osteocytes to make contact with each other. The **perforating canal** allows communication between the central canals of osteons.

Cancellous bone, also known as spongy bone, is found on the interior of all short, flat, and irregular bones as well as in the ends of long bones. Spongy bone is not composed of osteons. This bone tissue has spike-like structures known as **trabeculae** (trah-BEK-u-lah).

The compact bone tissue may be seen under the microscope. In the laboratory a microscopic demonstration of the osteon will be available for all students.

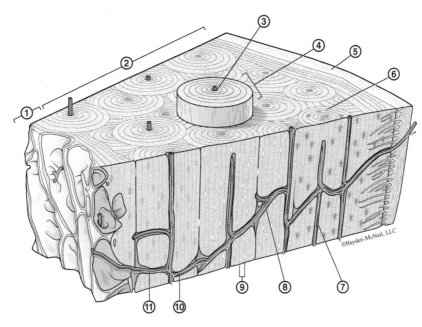

1. Spongy bone
2. Compact bone
3. Osteonic canal (central canal) containing vessels and nerves
4. Osteon
5. Periosteum
6. Osteocyte in lacuna
7. Osteonic canal
8. Perforating canal (Volkmann's canal)
9. Lamella (matrix)
10. Nerve
11. Blood vessel

©Hayden-McNeil, LLC

Figure 1.11. Compact Bone Tissue

①
②
③
④
©Hayden-McNeil, LLC

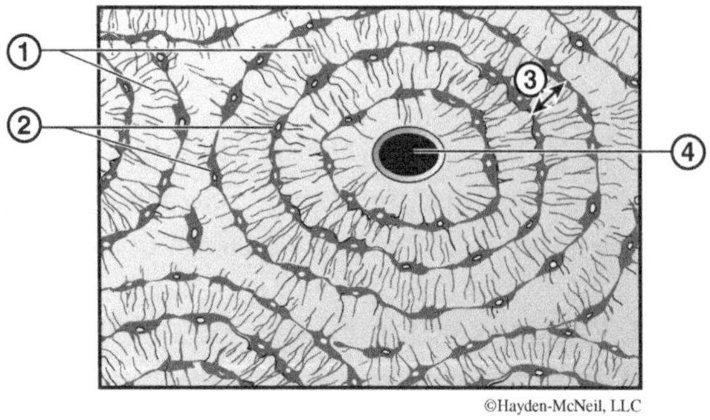

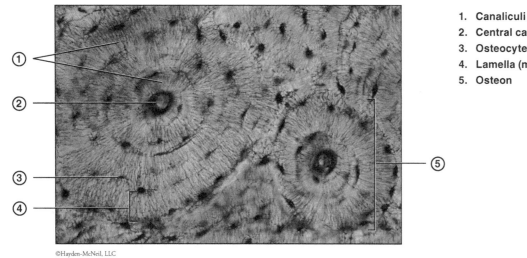

1. Canaliculi
2. Osteocytes in lacuna
3. Lamella (matrix)
4. Central (osteonic)

Figure 1.12. Structure of Osteon

①
②
③
④
⑤
©Hayden-McNeil, LLC

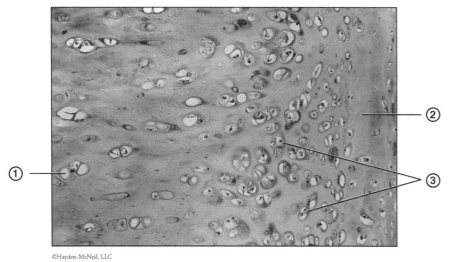

1. **Canaliculi**
2. **Central canal**
3. **Osteocyte in lacuna**
4. **Lamella (matrix)**
5. **Osteon**

Figure 1.13. Compact Bone Slide

①
②
③
©Hayden-McNeil, LLC

1. **Lacuna**
2. **Matrix/ground substance**
3. **Chondrocytes**

Figure 1.14. Hyaline Cartilage Slide

Structure of Long Bone

Long bones have a shaft called the **diaphysis** (die-AF-ah-sis). The shaft and the covering of the bone is compact bone. At each end of the shaft there is an enlarged portion called the **epiphyses** (ah-PIF-uh-seez). While children are growing there is a layer of cartilage between the diaphysis and the epiphyses, this is called the **epiphyseal plate** (epi-FIZZ-ee-ul). As children reach their adult height the cartilage is replaced by bone tissue and becomes the epiphyseal line. The outer surface of the ends is compact bone but inside these enlarged ends is cancellous bone. Covering the end of each epiphysis in living bone is an **articular cartilage** because these ends form articulations or joints with other bones.

Inside the diaphysis is a **medullary cavity** (MED-ular-ee KAV-ah-te) which contains marrow. In adults this marrow is yellow because it is not actively producing blood cells; in children it is red because it is producing blood cells. Lining the medullary cavity in living bone is the **endosteum** (end-OS-tee-um), a thin membrane. This membrane contains osteoblasts and osteoclasts. It also covers the surface of trabeculae in spongy bone. Covering the outside of living bone is a tough, fibrous **periosteum** (PER-ee-OS-tee-um). The periosteum assists in the formation and repair of bone tissue and contains osteoblasts as well as osteoclasts.

Bones have many grooves, depressions, and other types of bone markings where muscles attach or joints form. It is helpful to know the terminology before starting to look for these markings.

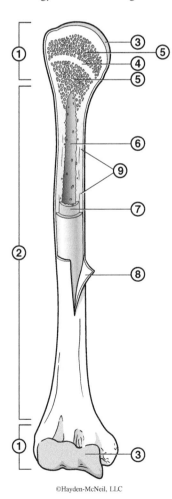

1. Epiphysis
2. Diaphysis
3. Articular cartilage
4. Epiphyseal line
5. Cancellous (spongy) bone
6. Medullary cavity
7. Endosteum
8. Periosteum
9. Compact bone

©Hayden-McNeil, LLC

Figure 1.15. Structure of Long Bone

Table 1.4: Bone Markings

Term	Description	Example
Condyle	Rounded articular projection	Condyles of femur
Crest	Narrow ridge of bone; usually prominent	Iliac crest
Epicondyle	Raised area on or above a condyle	Medial epicondyle of humerus
Facet	Smooth, nearly flat articular surface	Vertebral facet
Fissure	Narrow, slit-like opening	Inferior orbital fissure
Foramen pl. foramina	Round or oval opening through a bone	Foramen magnum of occipital bone
Fossa	Shallow, basin-like depression in a bone, often serving as an articular surface	Mandibular fossa of temporal bone
Groove	Furrow	Intertubercular groove
Head	Bony expansion carried on a narrow neck	Head of femur
Line	Narrow ridge of bone; less prominent than a crest	Ileopectineal line
Meatus	Canal-like passage	External auditory meatus
Process	Prominence or projection	Zygomatic process
Ramus	Arm-like bar of bone	Mandibular ramus
Sinus	Space within a bone, filled with air & lined with mucous membrane	Frontal sinus
Spine	Sharp, slender, often pointed projection	Anterior superior spine of ilium
Trochanter	Very large, blunt, irregularly shaped process	Greater trochanter of femur
Tubercle	Small rounded projection or process	Greater tubercle of humerus
Tuberosity	Large rounded projection; may be roughened	Ischial tuberosity

Section B – Appendicular Skeleton - Upper Limb

When discussing the skeleton it can be divided into two main groups: the **axial** (AK-se-al) skeleton and the **appendicular** (ap-en-DIK-u-lar) skeleton. The axial skeleton is made up of the bones that are found down the center of the skeleton. The appendicular skeleton is made up of the bones that are involved in the appendages or the arms and legs.

Before studying individual bones it is helpful to learn the position of each bone in the skeleton. After learning where each bone is located then move on to the bones of the appendicular skeleton.

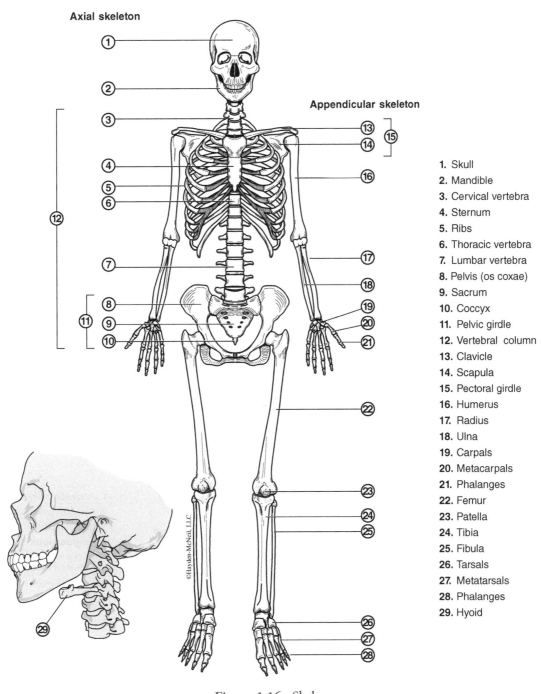

Axial skeleton

Appendicular skeleton

©Hayden-McNeil, LLC

1. Skull
2. Mandible
3. Cervical vertebra
4. Sternum
5. Ribs
6. Thoracic vertebra
7. Lumbar vertebra
8. Pelvis (os coxae)
9. Sacrum
10. Coccyx
11. Pelvic girdle
12. Vertebral column
13. Clavicle
14. Scapula
15. Pectoral girdle
16. Humerus
17. Radius
18. Ulna
19. Carpals
20. Metacarpals
21. Phalanges
22. Femur
23. Patella
24. Tibia
25. Fibula
26. Tarsals
27. Metatarsals
28. Phalanges
29. Hyoid

Figure 1.16. Skeleton

The appendicular skeleton consists of the bones associated with the limbs. In the upper limb this would include the bones of the arm, forearm, wrist, hand, as well as the bones that make up the pectoral girdle—the scapula and the **clavicle**.

The **scapula** (SKAP-u-la) is also known as the shoulder blade. It is held in place by muscles so the scapula is not normally fractured. It articulates with the clavicle to form the pectoral girdle.

On the upper lateral edge is the **glenoid** (GLEE-noyd) **cavity**. This is the articulation point for the head of the humerus. On the posterior surface is a ridge called the **spine** of the scapula. The spine runs from the medial or vertebral margin to the acromion process at the lateral end. There is a depression above the spine that is called the **supraspinous fossa**, and a depression below the spine that is called the **infraspinous fossa**.

The edge of the scapula nearest the vertebral column is known as the **medial** or **vertebral margin**. The edge of the scapula opposite the medial margin is known as the **lateral** or **axillary** (AK-sahler-ee) **margin**.

The **acromion** (ah-CRO-me-on) process is a broad, flat process at the end of the scapular spine. It articulates with the clavicle. On the anterior surface of the scapula, projecting anterior to the glenoid cavity is the **coracoid** (COR-uh-coyd) process which is an attachment point for some of the muscles of the arm.

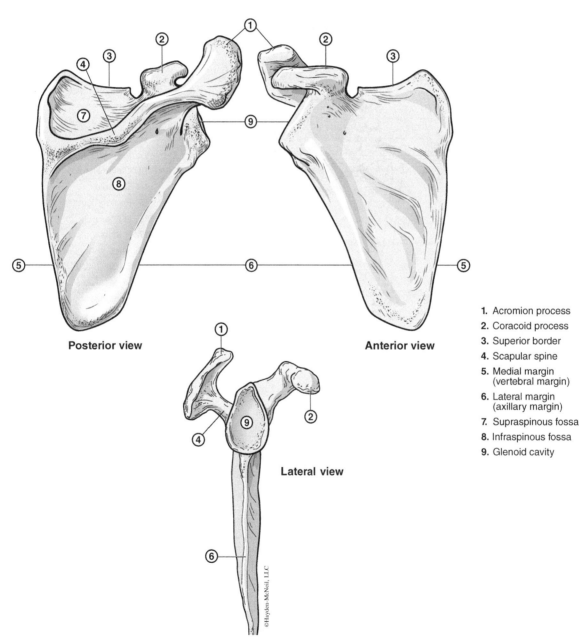

Posterior view

Anterior view

Lateral view

1. Acromion process
2. Coracoid process
3. Superior border
4. Scapular spine
5. Medial margin (vertebral margin)
6. Lateral margin (axillary margin)
7. Supraspinous fossa
8. Infraspinous fossa
9. Glenoid cavity

©Hayden-McNeil, LLC

Figure 1.17. Posterior, Anterior, and Lateral Scapula

The **clavicle** is an "S" shaped bone that is also known as the collarbone. It articulates with the manubrium of the sternum on the medial end and with the acromion process of the scapula on the lateral end.

The **humerus** is the bone of the upper arm. The **head** of the humerus is a smooth, rounded end that articulates with the glenoid cavity of the scapula to form the shoulder joint. Just below the articular surface of the head is the **anatomical neck** of the humerus. The **surgical neck** is the site where fractures frequently happen. It is located inferior to the greater and lesser tubercles.

There are two projections on the proximal end of the humerus that serve as attachment sites for the muscles of the rotator cuff. The larger projection is called the **greater tubercle** (TOO-burk-ul). It is found on the proximal lateral surface of the humerus. The smaller projection is called the **lesser tubercle**. It is found on the proximal anterior surface of the humerus. A roughened process on the lateral surface about mid-shaft of the humerus is the **deltoid tuberosity** (TOO-ber-os-ity), which is so named because it is the insertion site of the deltoid muscle.

On the distal end of the humerus there are several processes and a couple depressions that either act as attachment sites for muscles or serve as articulation points in the elbow. On the medial distal surface there is the grooved process called the **trochlea** (TROW-klee-ah) that articulates with the ulna. Above the trochlea is a knob-like projection that is known as the **medial epicondyle** (EP-IKON-dahl). Several flexor muscles of the forearm attach here. The tendons of these muscles can become inflamed and can be one of the causes of "tennis elbow" which can also be called epicondylitis.

On the lateral distal surface of the humerus is a rounded process called the **capitulum** (KAHPICH-uhlum). This process articulates with the head of the radius. Above the capitulum is a knob-like projection similar to the one above the trochlea. This is the **lateral epicondyle**. Several extensor muscles of the forearm attach to this epicondyle. The tendons of these muscles can become inflamed just like the tendons of the flexor muscles. This could also be a cause of "tennis elbow."

On the anterior surface of the humerus, superior to the trochlea, there is a depression called the **coronoid** (CAW-rahnoyd) **fossa** (FOS-ah). When the arm is flexed the coronoid process of the ulna fits into this fossa of the humerus.

On the posterior distal surface of the humerus there is another depression known as the **olecranon** (uh-LEC-rahnon) **fossa**. When the arm is extended the olecranon process of the ulna fits into this depression.

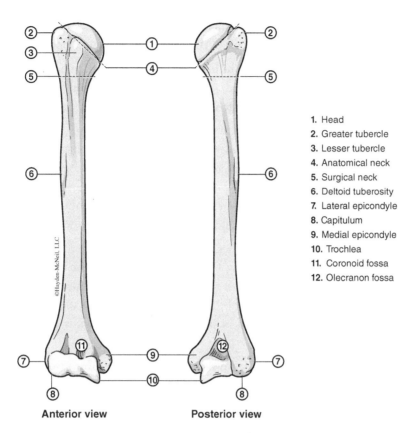

1. Head
2. Greater tubercle
3. Lesser tubercle
4. Anatomical neck
5. Surgical neck
6. Deltoid tuberosity
7. Lateral epicondyle
8. Capitulum
9. Medial epicondyle
10. Trochlea
11. Coronoid fossa
12. Olecranon fossa

Anterior view   Posterior view

Figure 1.18. Anterior and Posterior Humerus

The **ulna** is the medial bone in the forearm when the arm is in anatomical position. It articulates proximally with the trochlea of the humerus and the head of the radius and distally with the ulnar notch of the radius.

On the posterior proximal end of the ulna is the **olecranon process**. This process is the insertion site for the triceps brachii. The olecranon process fits into the olecranon fossa of the humerus when the forearm is extended. Below the olecranon process is the **trochlear** or **semilunar notch** which articulates with the trochlea of the humerus.

On the anterior proximal end of the ulna is the **coronoid process**. This process is the insertion site for the brachialis muscle. The coronoid process fits into the coronoid fossa of the humerus when the forearm is flexed.

On the lateral proximal end of the ulna is the **radial notch**. This depression allows the head of the radius to rest against the ulna. This articulation allows the radius to rotate and cross over the ulna. This movement is necessary for pronation of the hand.

On the distal end is the **head** of the ulna. This is a rounded structure that articulates with the radius. On the medial distal end of the ulna is the **stylus** or **styloid process**, a small pointed projection. This is the bump that can be palpated on the medial surface of the wrist.

The **radius** is the bone on the lateral side of the forearm when in anatomical position. The rounded proximal end of the radius that articulates with the ulna is the **head** of the radius. The **neck** of the radius is the constricted area distal to the head.

On the anteromedial surface of the radius there is a roughened area called the **radial tuberosity** (TOO-BAHROS-itee). This is the insertion point of the biceps brachii muscle.

On the lateral surface of the distal end of the radius there is a pointed projection known as the **stylus** or **styloid** (STY-loyd) **process** of the radius. This is the bump felt on the lateral surface of the wrist.

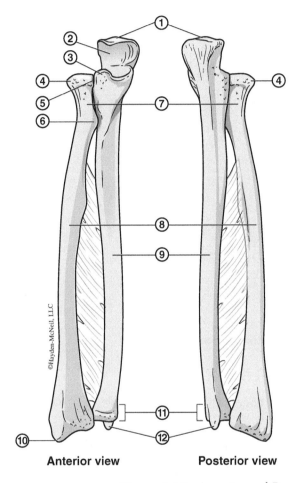

1. Olecranon process
2. Trochlear notch
3. Coronoid process
4. Head of radius
5. Radial notch
6. Radial tuberosity
7. Neck of radius
8. Radius
9. Ulna
10. Stylus (styloid process) of radius
11. Head of ulna
12. Stylus (styloid process) of ulna

Anterior view   **Posterior view**

Figure 1.19. Anterior and Posterior Radius and Ulna

The bones of the wrist are known as the **carpal bones**. There are 8 of these bones arranged in two rows. Proximally these bones articulate with the ulna and radius. Distally they articulate with the metacarpals. The bones of the palm of the hand are called the **metacarpal** (MET-ah-KAR-pahl) **bones**. There are 5 of these bones. These articulate distally with the **phalanges** (fah-LAN-jeez), the bones of the fingers. There are a total of 14 phalanges in each hand. The thumb has two phalanges and each finger has three phalanges.

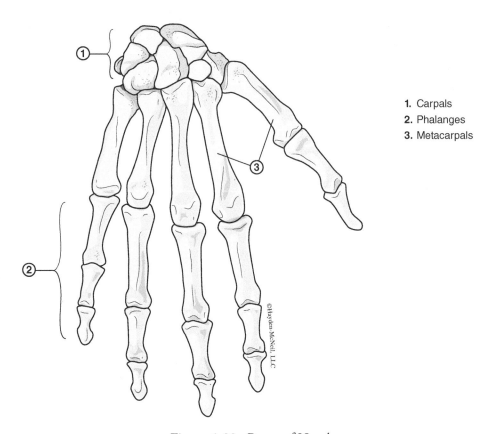

1. Carpals
2. Phalanges
3. Metacarpals

©Hayden-McNeil, LLC

Figure 1.20. Bones of Hand

SECTION C – APPENDICULAR SKELETON - LOWER LIMB

The appendicular skeleton of the lower limb includes the bones of the thigh, leg, ankle, foot, as well as the bones that make up the pelvis—the os coxae (OS COX-ee).

Each **os coxa**, or the hip bone, is formed by the fusion of three bones, the **ilium** (ILL-ee-um), **ischium** (ISS-kee-um) and **pubis** (PYOU-bis). The two os coxae are fused posterior to the sacrum and coccyx. This forms the **pelvic girdle**.

The ilium is the largest and most superior of the three bones. The pubis is the anterior portion of the os coxa and the ischium is the lowest portion of the os coxa. The three bones come together to form a cup-like structure known as the **acetabulum** (ASS-AHTAB-yahlum). This depression or cup on the lateral surface of the os coxa holds the ball-shaped head of the femur to form the hip joint.

The superior margin of the ilium is called the **iliac crest**. When placing the hands on the hips they rest on the iliac crests. On the posterior surface of the ilium it articulates with the sacrum at the **sacroiliac** (SAK-ro-IL-ee-ak) **joint**.

On the lateral surface of each ilium there are two projections. The uppermost, which is at the lateral end of the iliac crest, is called the **anterior superior iliac spine**. This is the attachment of the origin of the sartorius muscle. Below this the next projection is called the **anterior inferior iliac spine**. The projection ends just above the superior edge of the acetabulum. It is an attachment point for the rectus femoris.

On the posterior medial surface of each ilium, at the medial end of the iliac crest, there is a projection known as the **posterior superior iliac spine**. Below this projection is another projection called the **posterior inferior iliac spine**. Both these spines are on the posterior surface of the sacroiliac articulating surface.

Just below the posterior inferior iliac spine is the **greater sciatic** (sye-AT-ik) **notch**. This is a point of passage for a number of nerves and blood vessels.

The pubis is the anterior part of the pelvis on both sides. The pubic bones of each side meet anteriorly at a cartilaginous joint called the **symphysis pubis** (SIM-fie-sis PYOU-bis). The pubis has superior and inferior branches or rami that fuse with two rami of the ischium to form the **obturator foramen** (FORAY-mahn).

The ischium is the posterior, inferior portion of the pelvis. Rami of the ischium fuse with the pubis, as mentioned above. There is a rough projection on the lower portion of the ischium known as the **ischial tuberosity**. It is this projection that the body rests on when sitting. It is also the point of origin for the hamstring muscles of the thigh. Above the ischial tuberosity is a pointed projection called the **ischial spine**. It is just above the lesser sciatic notch.

Table 1.5: Differences between Female and Male Pelvis

NAME OF BONE	FEMALE	MALE
Obturator foramen	Oval	Round
Sacrum	Wider, shorter, accentuated sacral curve	Narrow, longer
Coccyx	More movable, straighter	Less movable, curves ventrally
Pelvic inlet	Wider, oval	Narrower, heart shaped
Pelvic outlet	Wider, ischial tuberosity shorter and farther apart	Narrower, ischial tuberosity longer, sharper, and point medially

Pelvis (os coxae)

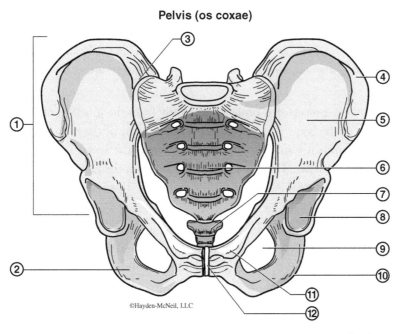

1. Ilium
2. Ischium
3. Sacroiliac joint
4. Iliac crest
5. Iliac fossa
6. Sacrum
7. Coccyx
8. Acetabulum
9. Obturator foramen
10. Ischial tuberosity
11. Pubis
12. Symphysis pubis

©Hayden-McNeil, LLC

Figure 1.21. Anterior View of Pelvis

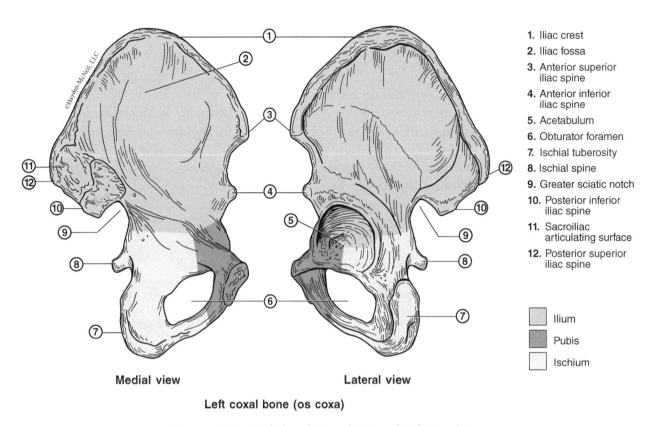

1. Iliac crest
2. Iliac fossa
3. Anterior superior iliac spine
4. Anterior inferior iliac spine
5. Acetabulum
6. Obturator foramen
7. Ischial tuberosity
8. Ischial spine
9. Greater sciatic notch
10. Posterior inferior iliac spine
11. Sacroiliac articulating surface
12. Posterior superior iliac spine

Ilium
Pubis
Ischium

Medial view   **Lateral view**

Left coxal bone (os coxa)

Figure 1.22. Medial and Lateral View of Left Coxal Bone

The **femur** is the longest, heaviest, and strongest bone in the body. It is the bone of the thigh. It has a rounded ball-like **head** that articulates with the acetabulum of the pelvis. Extending laterally from the head is the **neck** of the femur. This connects the head with the shaft. This neck is the weakest part of the femur and is the most common site of a "broken hip."

The **greater trochanter** (TRO-kan-tur) is a large process that projects superiorly from the junction of the neck and shaft of the femur. It is on the lateral surface of the bone. It is an insertion site for some of the muscles of the pelvis and buttocks. On the medial surface of the femur is a smaller projection known as the **lesser trochanter**. This is the insertion site of the psoas major and iliacus muscles. There is a roughened ridge on the lateral surface extending from the base of the greater trochanter, this is the **gluteal** (GLUE-tee-ul) **tuberosity**. This is an insertion site for the gluteus maximus.

On the distal end of the femur are two large rounded processes. On the medial surface is the **medial condyle** and on the lateral surface is the **lateral condyle**. These condyles articulate with the condyles of the tibia. Superior to the condyles are the **medial epicondyle** and **lateral epicondyle**. These are attachment points for ligaments and muscles.

On the anterior distal end there is a smooth **patellar surface** where the femur articulates with the patella or the kneecap.

The **patella** (PAH-tell-ah) is the bone that forms the kneecap. This bone is embedded in the tendon of the quadriceps femoris muscle. As a result of being embedded in the tendon it is classified as a **sesamoid** (SES-ah-moyd) bone. The patella protects the knee joint anteriorly. It also improves the leverage of the thigh muscles that extend across the knee joint.

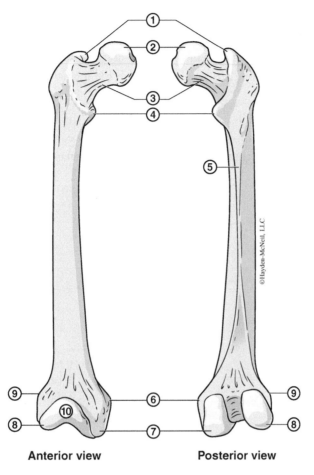

1. Greater trochanter
2. Head of femur
3. Neck of femur
4. Lesser trochanter
5. Gluteal tuberosity
6. Medial epicondyle
7. Medial condyle
8. Lateral condyle
9. Lateral epicondyle
10. Patellar surface

Anterior view   **Posterior view**

Figure 1.23. Anterior and Posterior Femur

The larger bone on the medial side of the leg is the **tibia** (TIB-ee-ah). It is known as the shinbone. It is the weight-bearing bone of the leg. On the proximal end there are two large processes: the **medial condyle** which articulates with the medial condyle of the femur and the **lateral condyle** which articulates with the lateral condyle of the femur and the head of the fibula.

Just below the condyles on the anterior surface of the tibia there is a roughened protrusion called the **tibial tuberosity**. This is the site where the patellar ligament attaches.

On the medial surface of the distal end of the tibia there is a large bony prominence known as the **medial malleolus** (mah-LEE-oh-lus). This is the bump found on the medial surface of the ankle. The malleolus articulates with the medial surface of the talus, which is one of the tarsal bones of the foot.

The smaller bone on the lateral side of the leg is the **fibula** (FIB-yah-lah). It is not a weight-bearing bone in the leg. The proximal end has an enlargement known as the **head**. This head articulates superiorly with the lateral condyle of the tibia. The fibula does not articulate with the femur.

On the lateral surface of the distal end of the fibula there is a bony projection called the **lateral malleolus**. This is the bump found on the lateral surface of the ankle. This malleolus articulates with the lateral surface of the talus.

The ankle consists of seven bones known as the **tarsals** (TAHR-sahls). The weight of the body is concentrated in two of these bones. The heel bone, which is the largest of the tarsals is the **calcaneus** (kal-KAY-nee-us). This bone helps support the weight and serves as an insertion point for the gastrocnemius and soleus muscles. The large bone on the top of the foot is the **talus** (TA-lus). This bone articulates with both the medial and the lateral malleoli to form the ankle joint.

The instep of the foot consists of five **metatarsal** (MET-ah-TAHR-sahl) bones. The distal heads of these bones form the ball of the foot. The toes of the foot consist of fourteen **phalanges**. The great toe contains two phalanges and all other toes contain three. These phalanges are shorter but otherwise similar to the phalanges of the fingers.

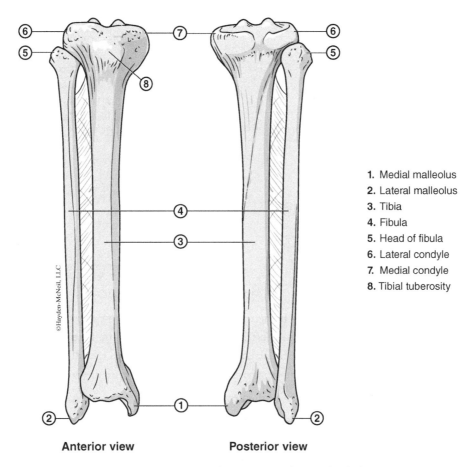

1. Medial malleolus
2. Lateral malleolus
3. Tibia
4. Fibula
5. Head of fibula
6. Lateral condyle
7. Medial condyle
8. Tibial tuberosity

Anterior view   **Posterior view**

Figure 1.24. Anterior and Posterior Tibia and Fibula

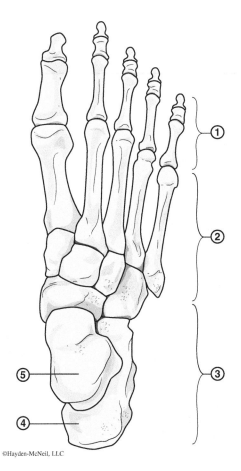

1. Phalanges
2. Metatarsals
3. Tarsals
4. Calcaneus
5. Talus

©Hayden-McNeil, LLC

Figure 1.25. Bones of the Foot

SECTION D – AXIAL SKELETON - VERTEBRAL COLUMN

The axial skeleton is made up of the bones that are found down the center of the skeleton. This consists of the skull, vertebral column, and the rib cage.

The vertebral column extends from the skull to the pelvis. It is the major support of the axial skeleton. It protects the spinal cord but allows the nerves to leave. There are four curvatures to the vertebral column: cervical, thoracic, lumbar, and sacral. The cervical and lumbar curvatures are convex, while the thoracic and sacral curvatures are concave.

Vertebra (VER-tah-brah) (pl. vertebrae)

The vertebrae are the bones that form the spine. There are a total of thirty-three (33) vertebrae: seven (7) cervical, twelve (12) thoracic, five (5) lumbar, five (5) fused to form the sacrum, and four (4) fused to form the coccyx.

There are several parts to each vertebra. The **body** is the largest part of the vertebra. Between each body there is an **intervertebral** (IN-TAHVER-tahbral) **disk** of cartilage. This is a disk of fibrocartilage that serves to cushion and act as a shock absorber. There is no intervertebral disk between the atlas and axis, and between the sacrum and coccyx. The **vertebral** or **neural arch** is the curve of bone formed by the pedicle and lamina of the vertebra. It is responsible for the protection of the spinal cord.

The **pedicle** (PED-ik-cul) is a bony projection that extends posteriorly from each side of the vertebral body. It connects the body with the transverse process. Each pedicle has superior and inferior vertebral notches which form the intervertebral foramen.

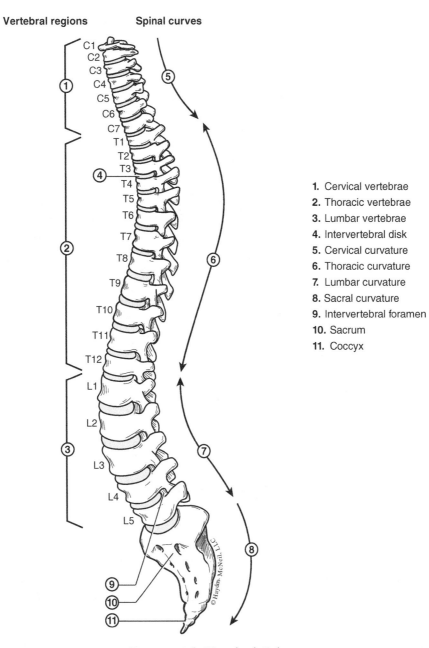

Vertebral regions   **Spinal curves**

1. Cervical vertebrae
2. Thoracic vertebrae
3. Lumbar vertebrae
4. Intervertebral disk
5. Cervical curvature
6. Thoracic curvature
7. Lumbar curvature
8. Sacral curvature
9. Intervertebral foramen
10. Sacrum
11. Coccyx

Figure 1.26. Vertebral Column

The **lamina** (LAM-in-uh) is a plate of bone that is an extension of the pedicle. It is located between the transverse process and the spinous process of the vertebra. The laminae actually meet in the midline to form the spinous process.

The **transverse process** is a lateral process that extends from the junction of the pedicle and the lamina of the vertebra. It is a site for muscle attachment. On the transverse process of the thoracic vertebrae, there is an articular surface for the ribs.

The **spinous process** is a posterior process of the vertebrae that protrudes midline and projects inferiorly. It is an important site of muscle attachment. The spinous process takes on different appearances depending on the region of the vertebral column. For example, the spinous processes of cervical vertebrae 2–6 are split in two.

The **intervertebral foramen** is an opening between the pedicles of adjacent vertebrae. It is formed by adjacent inferior and superior intervertebral notches. This opening is for the passage of the spinal nerves and blood vessels.

The **superior** and **inferior articulating surfaces** are projections from the vertebral arch of each vertebra. Each articulating surface is covered with an articular cartilage. This is a joint between adjacent vertebrae.

The **vertebral** or **spinal foramen** is the opening formed by the body and the vertebral arch of the cervical, thoracic, and lumbar vertebrae. It contains the spinal cord, the meninges, epidural fat, and blood vessels.

Cervical vertebrae special features

Cervical vertebrae have **transverse foramina** (fah-RAM-ah-nah). These are openings in each transverse process. They allow for the passage of the vertebral arteries. The spinous processes on cervical vertebrae 2–6 are forked.

The first cervical vertebra is the **atlas**. The name is from the Greek Titan, Atlas. He was the Titan who carried the world on his shoulders. The first cervical vertebra carries the skull on its articular facets. The atlas has no vertebral body. It articulates superiorly with the occipital condyles of the skull and inferiorly with the odontoid process (dens) of the axis, the second cervical vertebra.

The second cervical vertebra is the **axis**. It has a process that extends superiorly from the vertebral body. This is the **odontoid** (O-DONT-oyd) **process** which is also known as the **dens**. This process articulates with the anterior vertebral arch of the atlas. The atlas and axis function as a unit. This articulation allows the head to rotate from side to side.

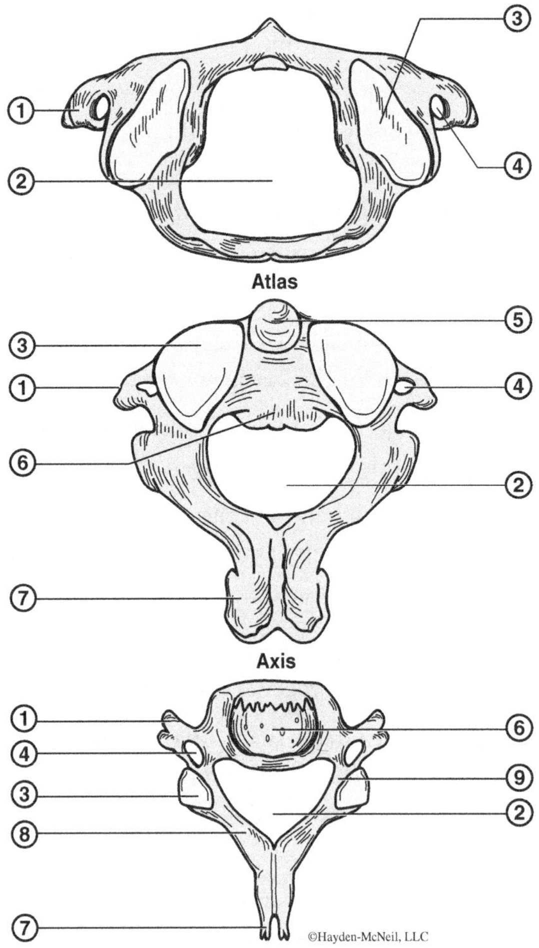

1. Transverse process
2. Spinal/vertebral foramen
3. Superior articulating surface
4. Transverse foramen
5. Dens/odontoid process
6. Body
7. Spinous process
8. Lamina
9. Pedicle

Atlas

Axis

©Hayden-McNeil, LLC

Figure 1.27. Cervical Vertebrae, Atlas, and Axis

Thoracic vertebrae special features

Thoracic vertebrae are characterized by spinous processes that are long and slender and project inferiorly. These vertebrae also have costal facets between the body and pedicle and on the transverse processes to articulate with the ribs.

Lumbar vertebrae special features

Lumbar vertebrae have short, blunt spinous processes that project posteriorly. These processes do not overlap the lumbar region. This allows for the insertion of a needle to perform a spinal tap.

Sacrum

The **sacrum** is a triangular bone that is formed by 5 fused vertebrae. This vertebra and the two os coxae form the pelvis. The sacrum articulates with these bones at the sacroiliac joints. It forms the posterior part of the pelvis.

Coccyx

The **coccyx** is the most inferior portion of the vertebral column. It is formed by the fusion of the four coccygeal (KOKSIJ-ee-ul) vertebrae. It articulates superiorly with the sacrum. The coccygeal vertebrae are simple; they do not have pedicles, laminae, or spinous processes. This portion of the vertebral column is known as the tailbone.

Cervical vertebrae

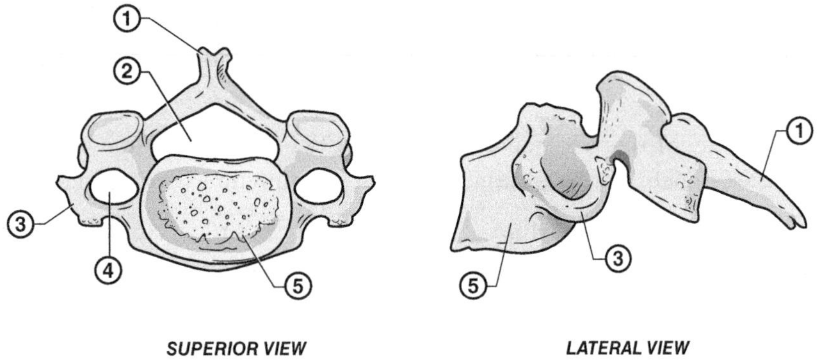

SUPERIOR VIEW   *LATERAL VIEW*

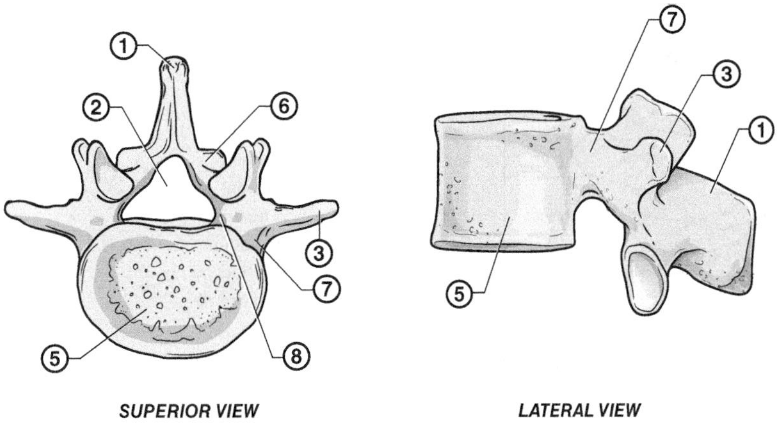

1. Spinous process
2. Spinal/vertebral foramen
3. Transverse process
4. Transverse foramen
5. Body
6. Lamina
7. Pedicle
8. Neural (vertebral) arch

Thoracic vertebrae

SUPERIOR VIEW   *LATERAL VIEW*

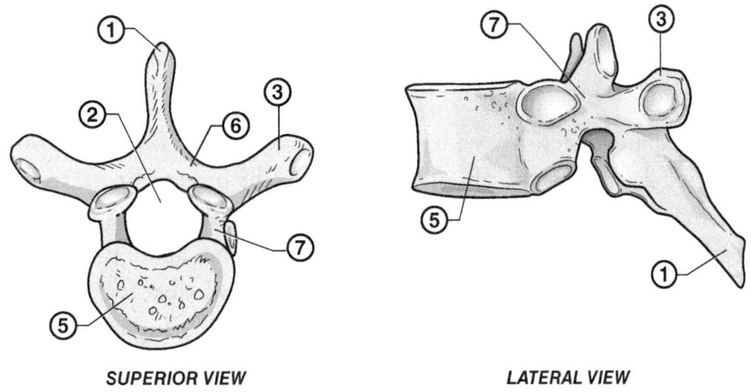

©Hayden-McNeil, LLC

Lumbar vertebrae

SUPERIOR VIEW   *LATERAL VIEW*

Figure 1.28. Typical Cervical, Thoracic, and Lumbar Vertebrae

SECTION E – AXIAL SKELETON—RIB CAGE

The rib cage consists of the sternum, twelve pairs of ribs, and the thoracic vertebrae. The thoracic vertebrae were discussed in the previous section so this section will only address the sternum and the ribs. This is a cone-shaped structure that protects the lungs and the heart.

The broad flat bone in the middle of the anterior thoracic wall is the **sternum** (STUR-num) or the breastbone. It is formed by three fused bones. The first seven pairs of ribs are attached to the sternum directly via costal cartilages.

The superior portion of the sternum is called the **manubrium** (MAHNOO-BREE-um). It articulates with the clavicles laterally. The first pair of ribs also articulate with the manubrium. It is one of the sites of attachment for the sternocleidomastoid muscle.

The middle part of the sternum is known as the **body**. It makes up most of the sternum, and ribs 2–7 articulate laterally with it. This portion of the sternum is the site of hand placement during CPR.

The articulation between the manubrium and the body form the **sternal angle**. These two bones meet at a slight angle at the level of the second rib. It is used as a reference point for locating the second intercostal space for listening to heart valve sounds. The inferior portion of the sternum is the **xiphoid** (ZYEF-oyd) process. It projects inferiorly over the abdominal cavity. It can be broken with incorrect hand placement during CPR.

There are twelve pairs of ribs. They all articulate posteriorly with the thoracic vertebrae. They curve downward and forward toward the anterior chest. The first seven pairs of ribs are called **true ribs** or **vertebrosternal ribs** because they attach directly to the sternum by means of a **costal cartilage**. The next five pairs of ribs are called **false ribs** because they either do not attach directly to the sternum or don't attach to the sternum at all. Rib pairs 8 though 10 attach to the rib above via a costal cartilage, so they are also called **vertebrochondral ribs**. Rib pairs 11 and 12 do not attach to any other rib or to the sternum. These two pairs of ribs are also called **floating ribs** or **vertebral ribs**.

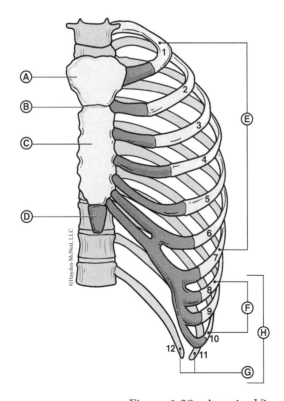

A. Manubrium
B. Sternal angle (notch)
C. Body of sternum
D. Xiphoid process
E. Ribs 1–7: true ribs
F. Ribs 8–10: vertebrochondral ribs
G. Ribs 11–12: floating ribs
H. Ribs 8–12: false ribs

Figure 1.29. Anterior View of Rib Cage

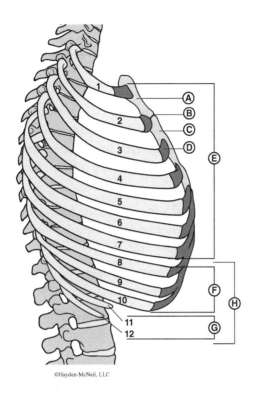

A. Manubrium
B. Sternal angle (notch)
C. Body of sternum
D. Costal cartilage
E. Ribs 1–7: true (vertebrosternal) ribs
F. Ribs 8–10: vertebrochondral ribs
G. Ribs 11–12: floating (vertebral) ribs
H. Ribs 8–12: false ribs

©Hayden-McNeil, LLC

Figure 1.30. Lateral View of Rib Cage

SECTION F – AXIAL SKELETON - SKULL

The skull consists of two sets of bones: the bones that make up the cranium, which encloses and protects the brain, and the facial bones. There are eight cranial bones and fourteen facial bones.

Table 1.6: Cranial and Facial Bones

CRANIAL BONES	FACIAL BONES
Frontal bone – 1	Maxilla – 2
Parietal bones – 2	Palatine bones – 2
Occipital bone – 1	Zygomatic bones – 2
Temporal bones – 2	Lacrimal bones – 2
Sphenoid bone – 1	Nasal bones – 2
Ethmoid bone – 1	Vomer – 1
	Inferior Nasal Conchae – 2
	Mandible – 1

Cranial Bones

The anterior bone of the skull is the **frontal bone**. In the skull the articulations between the bones are immovable joints called sutures. The frontal bone articulates posteriorly with the two parietal bones at the **coronal suture**. It also articulates inferiorly with the ethmoid, sphenoid, and zygomatic bones. Anteriorly there are articulations with the maxilla, nasal, and lacrimal bones.

The superior lateral walls of the cranium are formed by the two **parietal bones**. These two bones articulate with each other in the midline at the **sagittal suture**. As mentioned above, the parietal bones also articulate anteriorly with the frontal bone at the coronal suture. Posteriorly it articulates with the occipital bone at the **lambdoidal** (LAMDOI-dahl) **suture**. The parietal bone articulates inferiorly with the greater wing of the sphenoid and with the temporal bone at the **squamosal** (SKWA-mow-sul) **suture**.

The inferior lateral walls of the cranium are formed by the **temporal bones**. There are several important markings on the temporal bones. The **zygomatic** (ZEYEGO-MAT-ik) **process** is a bridge-like projection off the temporal bone that joins the zygomatic bone anteriorly to form the **zygomatic arch** or the cheekbone.

On the inferior surface of the zygomatic process is a depression known as the **mandibular** or **glenoid fossa** which articulates with the mandibular condyle of the mandible to form the temporomandibular joint.

Below the zygomatic process on the lateral surface of the temporal bone is the **external auditory** or **acoustic meatus** (ME-A-tus). This is the canal that leads to the middle ear. It allows sound to reach the tympanic membrane or eardrum.

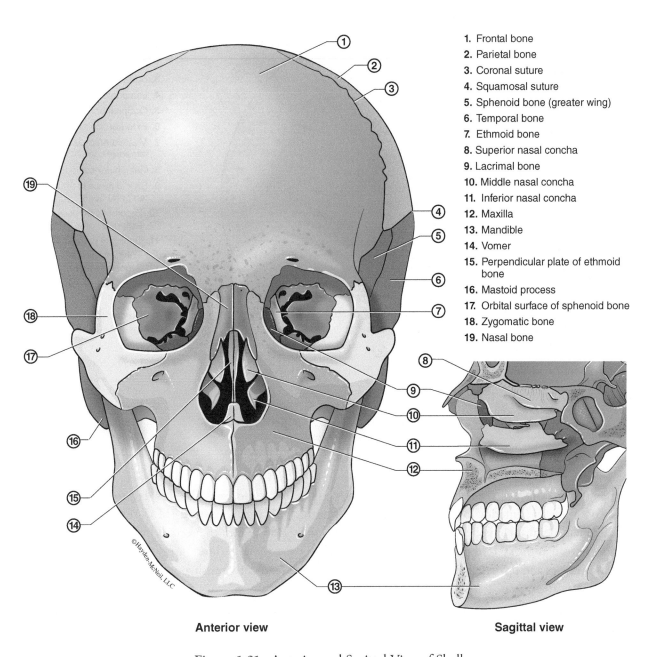

1. Frontal bone
2. Parietal bone
3. Coronal suture
4. Squamosal suture
5. Sphenoid bone (greater wing)
6. Temporal bone
7. Ethmoid bone
8. Superior nasal concha
9. Lacrimal bone
10. Middle nasal concha
11. Inferior nasal concha
12. Maxilla
13. Mandible
14. Vomer
15. Perpendicular plate of ethmoid bone
16. Mastoid process
17. Orbital surface of sphenoid bone
18. Zygomatic bone
19. Nasal bone

Anterior view

Sagittal view

Figure 1.31. Anterior and Sagittal View of Skull

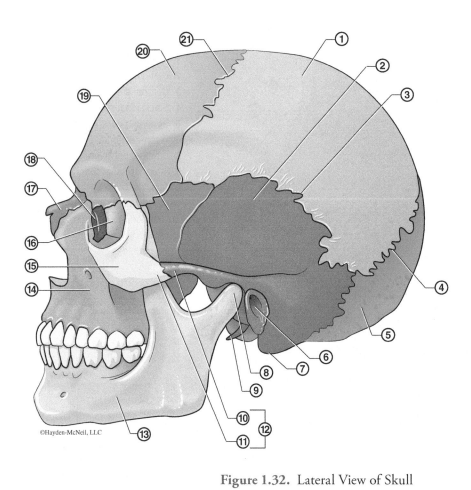

1. Parietal bone
2. Temporal bone
3. Squamosal suture
4. Lambdoidal suture
5. Occipital bone
6. External acoustic meatus
7. Mastoid process of temporal bone
8. Mandibular condyle
9. Styloid process of temporal bone
10. Zygomatic process of temporal bone
11. Temporal process of zygomatic bone
12. Zygomatic arch
13. Mandible
14. Maxilla
15. Zygomatic bone
16. Ethmoid bone
17. Nasal bone
18. Lacrimal bone
19. Greater wing of sphenoid bone
20. Frontal bone
21. Coronal suture

©Hayden-McNeil, LLC

Figure 1.32. Lateral View of Skull

On the inferior surface of the temporal bone there are two important processes. The first is a rough rounded projection posterior and inferior to the external auditory meatus. This is the **mastoid** (MAS-toyd) **process**. This is an attachment point for muscles including the sternocleidomastoid muscle. The second projection is a needlelike structure known as the **styloid process**. It is found inferior to the external auditory meatus. It too is an attachment point for muscles and ligaments. In the laboratory this process is frequently missing or broken on the skull since it is a rather delicate process.

Also on the inferior surface of the temporal bone there is the **carotid** (KAHROT-id) **canal**, an opening for the passage of the internal carotid artery into the cranial cavity. This opening can be found medial to the styloid process. The **jugular foramen** is an opening between the temporal bone and the occipital bone that allows the passage of the internal jugular vein and cranial nerves IX, X, and XI. It can also be found medial to the styloid process.

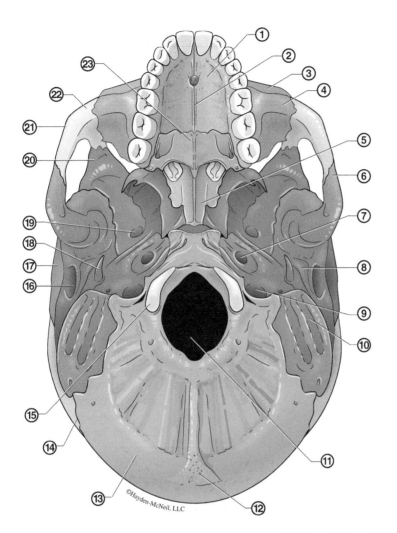

1. Palatine process of maxilla
2. Median palatine suture
3. Frontal bone
4. Maxilla
5. Vomer
6. Zygomatic process of temporal bone
7. Carotid canal
8. Mandibular/glenoid fossa
9. Jugular foramen
10. Mastoid process
11. Foramen magnum
12. External occipital protuberance
13. Occipital bone
14. Lambdoidal suture
15. Occipital condyle
16. External acoustic meatus
17. Temporal bone
18. Styloid process
19. Foramen ovale
20. Sphenoid bone
21. Zygomatic arch
22. Zygomatic bone
23. Palatine bone

©Hayden-McNeil, LLC

Figure 1.33. Inferior View of Skull

The back and floor of the skull is formed by the **occipital** (OKSIP-it-ahl) **bone**. It articulates with the parietal bones at the lambdoidal suture. The occipital bone also articulates with the temporal and sphenoid bones.

On the inferior surface of the occipital bone there is a large opening called the **foramen** (FORAY-mahn) **magnum**. The spinal cord and the vertebral arteries enter the cranium through this opening. Rounded projections lateral to the foramen magnum are the **occipital condyles**. These projections articulate with facets on the first cervical vertebra, the atlas.

The **sphenoid** (SFE-noyd) **bone** is a bat-shaped bone that spans the center portion of the skull. It is described as having a body, two greater wings, and two lesser wings. It articulates anteriorly with the zygomatic bone, superiorly with the frontal and parietal bones, and posteriorly with the temporal bone.

The **greater wings** of the sphenoid are on the exterior of the skull, anterior to the temporal bone. The greater wings form part of the outer wall of the orbits for the eyes and part of the internal lateral wall of the orbits.

The sphenoid bone is best observed looking into the floor of the cranium or looking at the inferior surface of the skull. Observing the sphenoid on the cranial floor there is a saddle-shaped region in the midline called the **sella turcica** (SEL-ah TUR-sikah) which means the Turkish saddle. The seat of the saddle is the **hypophyseal fossa** (HIPO-FIZE-ahl FOS-ah). The pituitary gland sits in this depression. The horns on the back of the saddle are the **dorsum sellae**.

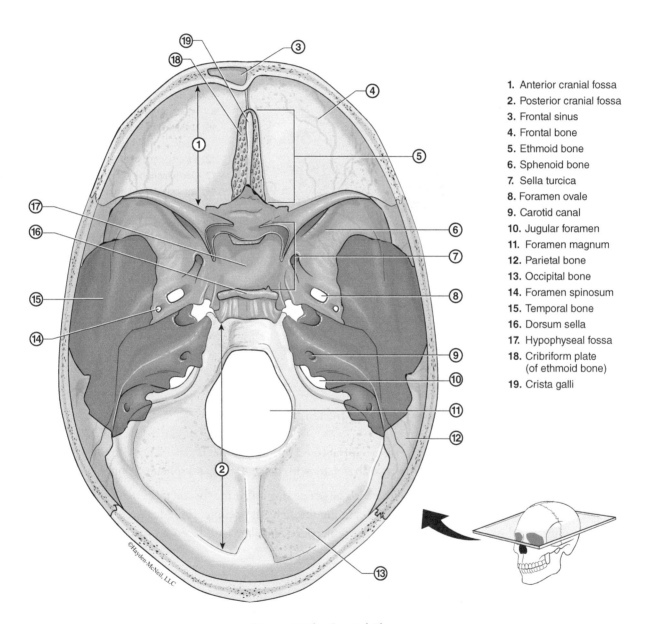

1. Anterior cranial fossa
2. Posterior cranial fossa
3. Frontal sinus
4. Frontal bone
5. Ethmoid bone
6. Sphenoid bone
7. Sella turcica
8. Foramen ovale
9. Carotid canal
10. Jugular foramen
11. Foramen magnum
12. Parietal bone
13. Occipital bone
14. Foramen spinosum
15. Temporal bone
16. Dorsum sella
17. Hypophyseal fossa
18. Cribriform plate (of ethmoid bone)
19. Crista galli

Figure 1.34. Cranial Floor

Openings in the base of the lesser wings are the **optic canals**. These openings allow the optic nerves to leave the eyes and approach the optic chiasm or chiasma.

Looking into the cranial floor there are three depressions: anterior cranial fossa, middle cranial fossa, and posterior cranial fossa. The **anterior cranial fossa** is formed by the orbital plates of the frontal, the cribriform plate of the ethmoid, and the small wings and front part of the body of the sphenoid. This is the region in the anterior portion of the cranial floor where the front lobes of the brain sit. The **middle cranial fossa** is formed mainly by the body of the sphenoid bone posterior to the lesser wing and the petrous portion of the temporal bone. This is the region where the temporal lobes and the hypothalamus are located. The **posterior cranial fossa** is located between the foramen magnum and tentorium cerebelli. This is the region in the posterior portion of the cranial floor where the cerebellum, pons, and medulla oblongata sit.

One of the hardest bones for students to identify is the **ethmoid** (ETH-moyd) **bone**. This is an irregular bone that is fused into the center of the skull. It forms the roof of the nasal cavity, the upper nasal septum, and part of the medial walls of the orbits.

The ethmoid bone extends superiorly into the floor of the cranium. The upper extension of this bone forms a vertical projection called the **crista galli** (KRIS-tah GAL-lee). This structure provides an attachment point for the dura mater, which helps secure the brain within the skull. On either side of the crista galli there are **cribriform** (KRIB-ri-FORM) **plates**. These plates contain many small foramina that allow the olfactory nerves to pass from the nose to the brain.

An inferior projection of the ethmoid bone forms the superior portion of the nasal septum; this is the **perpendicular plate** of the ethmoid. There are masses on either side of the perpendicular plate. Projections from these masses extend medially into the nasal cavities. These are the **superior concha** (KONG-kah) and **middle concha**. These structures increase the surface area in the nasal cavity to increase the ability of the nasal mucosa to adequately warm and humidify inhaled air.

Facial Bones

The lower jaw bone is the **mandible**, a U-shaped bone. It articulates with the mandibular fossa on the temporal bone to form the only freely moving joint in the skull. The horizontal portion of this bone that forms the chin is the **body**. The vertical projection of either side of the body is the **ramus** (RAY-mahs). The anterior portion of the ramus is the **coronoid process**. It serves as a site of the temporalis muscle attachment. The posterior rounded projection is the **mandibular condyle** which fits into the mandibular fossa on the temporal bone to form the temporomandibular joint (TMJ).

The upper jaw is the **maxilla** (MAKSIL-ah). Two bones fuse to form the upper jaw, and all bones except for the mandible articulate with the maxilla. So the maxillae can be considered major bones of the face. Projecting posteriorly from the maxilla are the **palatine processes**. These processes join together at the **median palatine suture**. The fused palatine process along with the palatine bone forms the roof of the mouth, which is the hard palate. The palatine process also forms the floor of the nasal cavity.

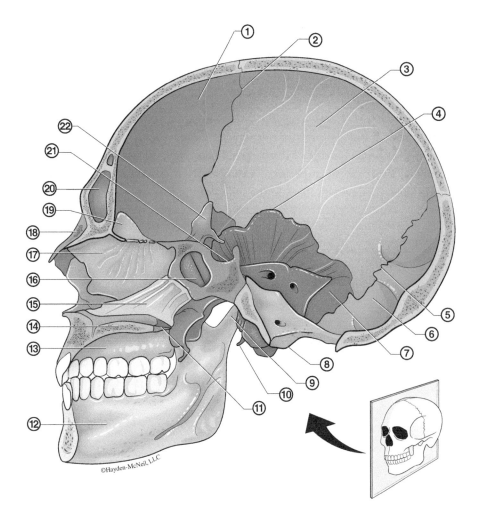

1. Frontal bone
2. Coronal suture
3. Parietal bone
4. Squamosal suture
5. Lambdoidal suture
6. Occipital bone
7. Temporal bone
8. Mastoid process
9. Mandibular condyle
10. Styloid process of temporal bone
11. Palatine bone
12. Mandible
13. Maxilla
14. Palatine process of maxilla
15. Vomer
16. Sphenoidal sinus (right)
17. Perpendicular plate of ethmoid bone
18. Nasal bone
19. Crista galli
20. Frontal sinus
21. Hypophyseal fossa of sella turcica
22. Sphenoid bone

©Hayden-McNeil, LLC

Figure 1.35. Sagittal View of Skull

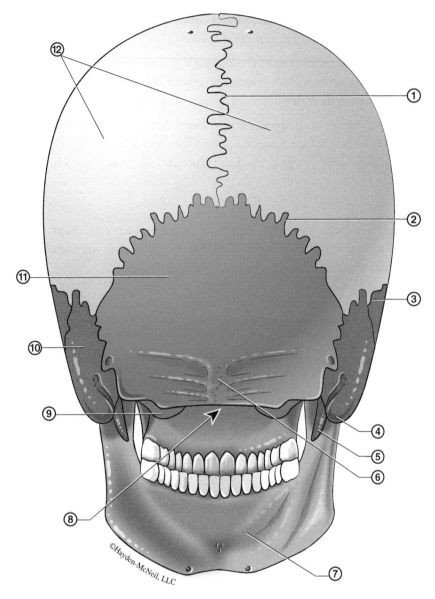

1. Sagittal suture
2. Lambdoidal suture
3. Squamosal suture
4. Mastoid process
5. Styloid process
6. External occipital protuberance
7. Mandible
8. Entrance to foramen magnum
9. Occipital condyle
10. Temporal bone
11. Occipital bone
12. Parietal bones

©Hayden-McNeil, LLC

Figure 1.36. Posterior View of Skull

The posterior portion of the hard palate is formed by the **palatine bones**. When these bones fail to fuse during development it leads to a cleft palate. The palatine bones articulate anteriorly with the palatine processes of the maxilla. Perpendicular portions of these bones help form the lateral walls of the nasal cavity.

The bones that form the bridge of the nose are the two **nasal bones**. These bones articulate with the frontal bone superiorly and the frontal process of the maxilla laterally.

Small rectangular bones that form the anterior portion of the orbit wall between the maxilla and the ethmoid are the **lacrimal** (LAK-rimul) **bones**. Each lacrimal bone has an opening, the **lacrimal fossa**, which serves as a passageway for the nasolacrimal duct which carries the tears from the eye to the nasal passage.

Separate bones on the lateral walls of the nasal cavity are the **inferior nasal conchae**. These serve the same purpose as the superior and middle conchae which are projections of the ethmoid bone.

Lateral to the maxilla is the **zygomatic bone** which forms part of the cheekbone. It articulates anteriorly with the maxilla, superiorly with the frontal bone, and posteriorly with the zygomatic process of the temporal bone. Together the zygomatic process and the zygomatic bone form the zygomatic arch, which is commonly called the cheekbone.

A thin bone that forms the posteroinferior part of the nasal septum is the **vomer**. It articulates superiorly with the perpendicular plate of the ethmoid bone and the body of the sphenoid bone; articulates inferiorly with the palatine processes of the maxilla and the horizontal plate of the palatine bone. This is another bone that is fused interiorly on the skull making it difficult to isolate.

Paranasal Sinuses

In four of the skull bones there are mucous-lined air cavities called sinuses. These cavities serve to lighten the bones and may act as resonance chambers. They lead into the nasal passages. The sinuses are located in the frontal, maxilla, sphenoid, and ethmoid bones. An inflammation of any of these cavities is sinusitis.

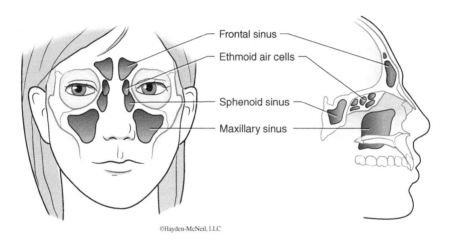

©Hayden-McNeil, LLC

Figure 1.37. Paranasal Sinuses

Hyoid Bone

The hyoid bone is not part of the skull but it also doesn't fit well into any of the other categories. It is a "U" shaped bone that is located in the neck superior to the larynx. It does not articulate with any other bones. It serves as a point of attachment for muscles of the tongue and neck.

MUSCLES

This section will focus on muscle tissue and some common skeletal muscles.

SECTION A – MUSCLE TISSUE

There are three types of muscle tissue: skeletal muscle, smooth muscle, and cardiac muscle.

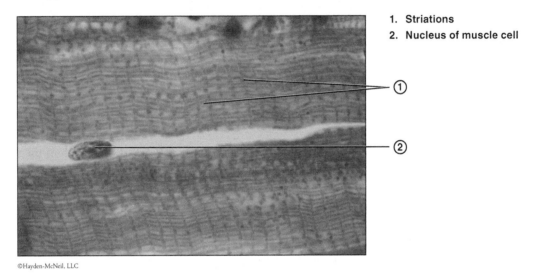

1. Striations
2. Nucleus of muscle cell

①

②

©Hayden-McNeil, LLC

Figure 1.38. Skeletal Muscle Slide

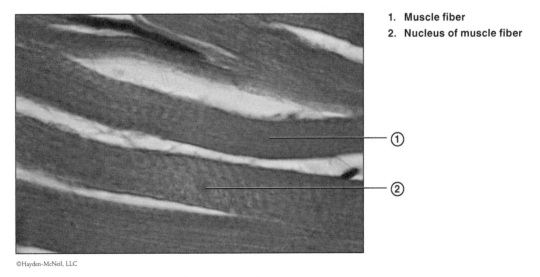

1. Muscle fiber
2. Nucleus of muscle fiber

①

②

©Hayden-McNeil, LLC

Figure 1.39. Cardiac Muscle Slide

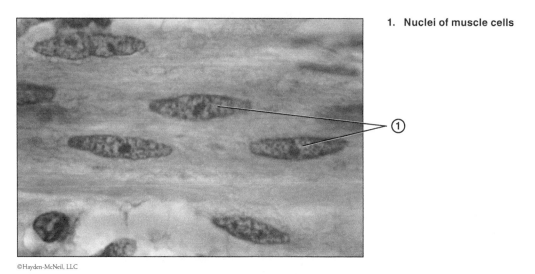

1. **Nuclei of muscle cells**

©Hayden-McNeil, LLC

Figure 1.40. Smooth Muscle Slide

Skeletal muscle is striated muscle under voluntary control. These muscle fibers extend the length of the muscle and are multinucleated, i.e., they have more than one nucleus. Skeletal muscles are attached to bone by tendons. They span joints, also known as articulations, and as a result are responsible for movement as well as joint stabilization. The origin of a muscle is the end attached to the bone that doesn't move, while the insertion of a muscle is the end that is attached to the bone that moves. For example, the origin of the biceps brachii muscle is on the scapula because this muscle does not move the scapula. The insertion of the biceps is on the radius because when the muscle contracts it pulls on the radius and results in the flexion of the forearm.

Cardiac muscle is only found in the walls of the heart. It is an involuntary muscle that is striated when observed under the microscope. The function of cardiac muscle is to pump blood through the body. Cardiac muscle will be addressed in Unit 3 when learning about the heart.

Smooth muscle is called smooth because it lacks striations. It is involuntary muscle that is located in the walls of hollow organs. This is the type of muscle found in blood vessels, airways, digestive organs, urinary bladder, and uterus to name a few. This type of muscle is found in structures in Unit 3 and 4.

SECTION B – MUSCLES OF THE FACE AND NECK

There are several muscles found in the face, some are involved in facial expression, others are involved in mastication or chewing. Two of the muscles that are responsible for mastication are the temporalis and the masseter. The muscles in the neck are responsible for moving the head and the vertebral column.

Muscles of the Face and Head
Temporalis (TEM-pur-alis)

The temporalis can be found on the surface of the temporal bone, above and in front of the ear. It is a muscle active in chewing. Tensing of this muscle is associated with the temporomandibular joint syndrome. This muscle can be felt in front of the ear when clenching the teeth.

Masseter (MASS-ih-tur)

This is a thick, flattened muscle just in front of the ear. It spans the jaw. It is the primary chewing muscle. This muscle can be felt in front of the ear when clenching the teeth.

Buccinator (BUK-se-NAY-tur)

This is a thin, flat muscle found under the masseter that forms the wall of the cheek. It functions to compress the cheek during chewing and pull the corner of the mouth laterally.

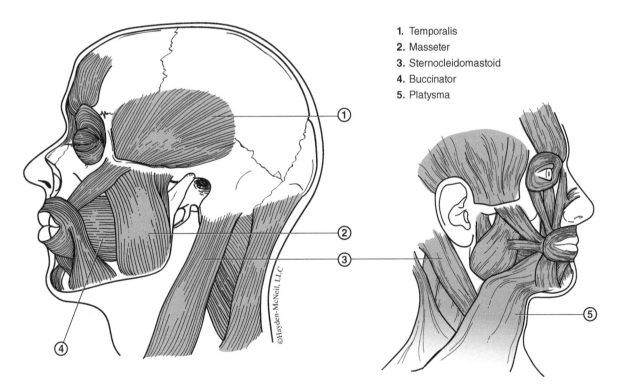

1. Temporalis
2. Masseter
3. Sternocleidomastoid
4. Buccinator
5. Platysma

©Hayden-McNeil, LLC

Figure 1.41. Muscles of the Face and Head

Muscles of the Neck

Sternocleidomastoid (STUR-no-KLEYE-doe-MAS-toyd)

This muscle is found on either side of the neck, extending on the diagonal from the chest to the mastoid process of the skull. When only one of the sternocleidomastoid muscles contracts it rotates the head towards the opposite side. When both muscles work together they flex the neck towards the chest. The sternocleidomastoid can raise the sternum and help with inhalation if the head is stabilized by other muscles.

Platysma (plah-TIZ-mah)

This is the surface muscle of the neck. This muscle is responsible for depressing the mandible and lower lip. It also tenses the skin over the lower neck. It is superficial to the sternocleidomastoid.

Table 1.7: Muscles of the Head, Face, and Neck

MUSCLE	ORIGIN	INSERT	ACTION
Face			
Temporalis	Temporal fossa	Coronoid process of mandible	Closes jaw; elevates and retracts mandible
Masseter	Zygomatic arch and maxilla	Angle and ramus of mandible	Closes jaw; elevates and protracts mandible
Buccinator	External alveolar margins of maxilla	Decussates at modiolus of mouth and interdigitates with opposite side	Aids mastication, tenses cheeks in blowing and whistling, aids closure of mouth
Neck			
Sternocleidomastoid	Manubrium of sternum; medial portion of clavicle	Mastoid process of temporal bone and superior nuchal line of occipital bone	Abducts, rotates, and flexes head
Platysma	Skin over lower neck and upper lateral chest	Inferior border of mandible and skin over lower face and mouth	Depresses and wrinkles skin of lower face and mouth. Aids forced depression of mandible

SECTION C – MUSCLES OF THE TRUNK

The muscles of the trunk would include muscles found on the chest, shoulder, back, and abdomen. These muscles are separated according to the area of the torso where they are found.

Muscles of the Chest

The muscles found on the chest can be involved in moving the arm, pectoral girdle, or the rib cage. The superficial muscles of the chest include the pectoralis major and the serratus anterior. These are involved in moving the arm and pectoral girdle. The deeper muscles of the chest include the external and internal intercostals which are involved in moving the rib cage.

Pectoralis major (PECK-tur-AL-is)

This is a large muscle that makes up the majority of the upper chest. It is fan-shaped and extends from the armpit to the middle of the thorax. The pectoralis major moves the arm. It is a target of most bodybuilders.

Serratus anterior (SER-RAT-us)

The muscle is found on the upper lateral aspect of the chest. It's origin on the ribs appears to give the muscle the look of the serrated edge of a knife. It is responsible for moving the pectoral girdle. It is the muscle that is used if the shoulder is moved forward when pushing something.

External intercostals (IN-ter-KOS-tahl)

These muscles are found between the ribs. The external intercostals are closer to the surface than the internal intercostals. The fibers of these muscles run obliquely downward and forward toward the sternum. These muscles are used to assist in inhalation.

Internal intercostals

These muscles are also found between the ribs. The internal intercostals are under the external intercostals. The fibers of these muscles run in the opposite direction of the external intercostals. These muscles are used in forceful exhalation as when blowing out the candles on the birthday cake.

Table 1.8: Muscles of the Chest

MUSCLE	ORIGIN	INSERT	ACTION
Face			
Pectoralis major	Clavicle, sternum, cartilage of ribs 1–7	Crest of greater tubercle	Flexes, adducts and medial rotates arm
Serratus anterior	Lateral aspect of ribs 1–8	Vertebral border of anterior surface of scapula	Laterally rotates and protracts scapula
External intercostals	Inferior border of rib above	Superior border of rib below	Elevates ribs; aids in inspiration
Internal intercostals	Superior border of rib below	Inferior border of rib above	Depresses ribs; aids in forced expiration

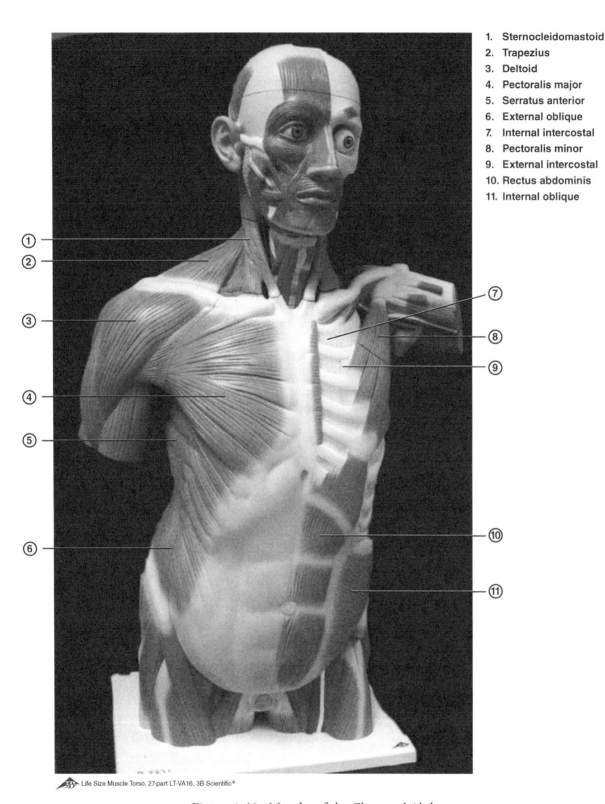

1. Sternocleidomastoid
2. Trapezius
3. Deltoid
4. Pectoralis major
5. Serratus anterior
6. External oblique
7. Internal intercostal
8. Pectoralis minor
9. External intercostal
10. Rectus abdominis
11. Internal oblique

Life Size Muscle Torso, 27-part LT-VA16, 3B Scientific®

Figure 1.42. Muscles of the Chest and Abdomen

Muscles of the Abdomen

The abdominal muscles in the anterior and lateral wall are layers of broad flattened muscles. Most muscles are directly supported by bone, but these muscles are not. They connect the ribs and the vertebral column to the pelvic girdle. There is a band of connective tissue that extends from the xiphoid process to the symphysis pubis which serves as an attachment point for some of the abdominal muscles. This connective tissue is known as the **linea alba** (LIN-ee-ah AL-bah).

When the abdominal muscles contract they decrease the volume of the abdominal cavity and increase the pressure inside. They can be used during forceful exhalation, and to assist in defecation, childbirth, and urination.

These muscles include the rectus abdominis and external obliques which are superficial muscles and the internal obliques and the transverse abdominis which are deeper muscles.

Rectus abdominis (REK-tahs AB-dom-in-us)

These are two muscles that are long straight muscles on the surface of the abdomen. They can be found on each side of the linea alba. These are the muscles individuals are referring to when they talk about "six-pack abs."

External oblique (ik-STUR-nahl ah-BLEEK)

This muscle is on the lateral surface of the abdomen. The fibers run downward and medially. The fibers run as if one is putting the hands in the pants pockets.

Internal oblique (in-TUR-nahl ah-BLEEK)

This muscle is on the lateral surface of the abdomen beneath the external oblique. The fibers run at a right angle to the external oblique.

Transverse abdominis (trans-VURS AB-dom-in-us)

This is the deepest muscle of the abdominal wall. These muscles run across the abdomen from each side to the linea alba.

Table 1.9: Muscles of the Abdomen

MUSCLE	ORIGIN	INSERT	ACTION
Rectus abdominis	Pubic crest and symphysis	Xiphoid process and costal cartilages of ribs 5–7	Flexes vertebral column, compresses abdomen
External oblique	Ribs 5–12	Linea alba, pubic crest, and tubercles and iliac crest	Compresses abdomen, laterally rotates trunk
Internal oblique	Lumbar fascia, iliac crest, inguinal ligament	Linea alba, pubic crest, and costal cartilages of last 3 ribs	Compresses abdomen, laterally rotates trunk
Transverse abdominis	Inguinal ligament, iliac crest, cartilages of last 5–6 ribs and lumbar fascia	Linea alba and pubic crest	Compresses abdomen, laterally rotates trunk

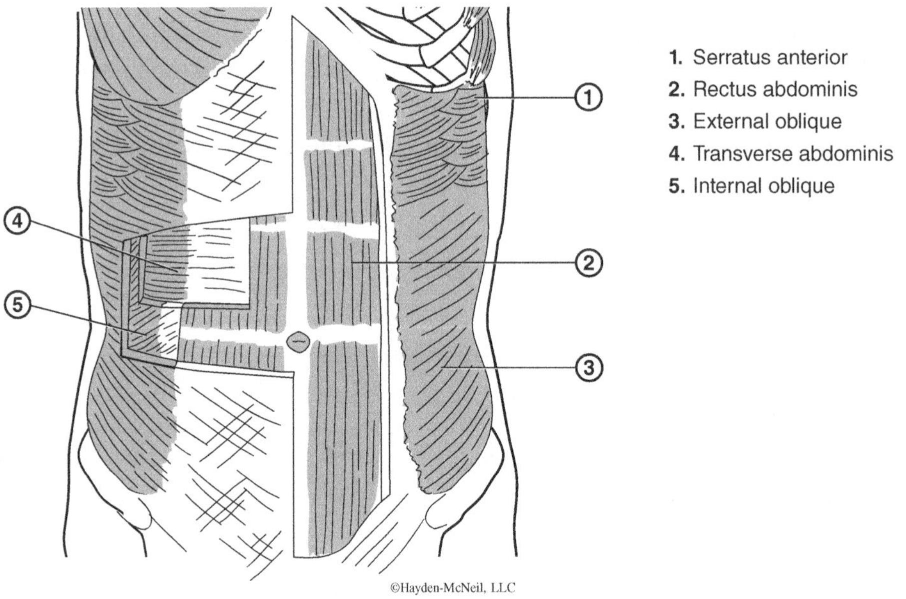

Figure 1.43. Abdominal Muscles

1. Serratus anterior
2. Rectus abdominis
3. External oblique
4. Transverse abdominis
5. Internal oblique

©Hayden-McNeil, LLC

Muscles of the Shoulder and Back

The muscles of the shoulder and back are responsible for moving the pectoral girdle and the arm. Most of the muscles discussed here are superficial; a couple, the supraspinatus and subscapularis, are deeper muscles. Four of these muscles are known as the rotator cuff: the subscapularis, supraspinatus, infraspinatus, and teres minor. The rotator cuff muscles are responsible for holding the humerus in the shoulder joint. When there is a shoulder injury these muscles are frequently involved.

Trapezius (trah-PEE-zee-us)

This is a diamond shaped surface muscle found in the upper back. This is the muscle used when shrugging the shoulder. It can also be used to hyperextend the neck.

Latissimus dorsi (lah-TISS-ih-mus DOR-sigh)

This is a large muscle in the lumbar region of the back. It arises in the back but inserts on the humerus so it is responsible for movement of the shoulder. This is the muscle that is used when swimming, climbing, and rowing.

Teres major (TARE-eez)

This is the most inferior muscle on the posterior surface of the scapula. It connects the scapula to the humerus.

Teres minor

This muscle is found on the posterior surface of the scapula between the teres major and the infraspinatus. This muscle and the infraspinatus rotate the arm laterally.

Infraspinatus (IN-fra-spin-AT-us)

The infraspinatus is found on the posterior surface of the scapula, inferior to the scapular spine.

Supraspinatus (SOUP-rah-spin-AT-us)

This muscle is found on the posterior surface of the scapula, superior to the scapular spine. It is found under the trapezius muscle.

Subscapularis (SUB-skap-you-LAR-is)

This muscle covers the anterior surface of the scapula. The subscapularis rotates the arm medially.

Deltoid (DEL-toyd)

This muscle is responsible for the roundness of the shoulder. It is the muscle mass that is the site of intramuscular injections.

Coracobrachialis (core-AK-oh-BRAY-key-AL-is)

This muscle arises on the coracoid process of the scapula. It can be found by looking in the axillary region and the medial surface of the humerus.

Table 1.10: Muscles of the Shoulder and Back

MUSCLE	ORIGIN	INSERT	ACTION
Trapezius	Posterior occipital bone, ligamentum nuchae, spines of C7–T12	Acromion and spinous process of scapula; lateral 1/3 of clavicle	Extends and adducts head, rotates, adducts, and fixes scapula
Latissmus dorsi	T7–12, L1–5, S1–5, crest of ilium, ribs 10–12	Tubercular groove of humerus	Extension, adduct and medially rotate arm, depresses the shoulder
Teres major	Posterior surface at inferior angle of scapula	Crest of lesser tubercle of humerus	Extends, medially rotates and adducts arm
Teres minor	Lateral margin of scapula	Greater tubercle of humerus	Extends, laterally rotates and adducts arm; stabilizes shoulder joint
Infraspinatus	Infraspinous fossa	Greater tubercle of humerus	Extension, lateral rotation of arm; stabilizes shoulder joint
Supraspinatus	Supraspinous fossa of scapula	Greater tubercle of humerus	Abduction of arm; stabilizes shoulder joint
Subscapularis	Subscapular fossa of scapula	Lesser tubercle of humerus	Medially rotate arm; stabilizes shoulder joint
Deltoid	Lateral 1/3 of clavicle, acromion and spine of scapula	Deltoid tuberosity of humerus	Adducts arms, flexes, extends, medially and laterally rotates arm
Coracobrachialis	Coracoid process of scapula	Midmedial shaft of humerus	Flexes and adducts arm

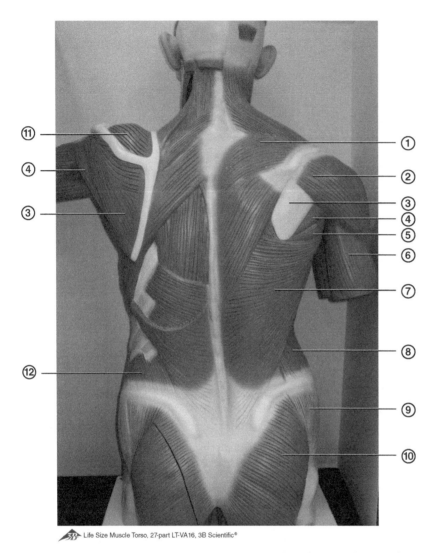

Life Size Muscle Torso, 27-part LT-VA16, 3B Scientific®

1. Trapezius
2. Deltoid
3. Infraspinatus
4. Teres minor
5. Teres major
6. Triceps brachii
7. Latissimus dorsi
8. External oblique
9. Gluteus medius
10. Gluteus maximus
11. Supraspinatus
12. Internal oblique

Figure 1.44. Muscles of the Back and Shoulder

SECTION D – MUSCLES OF THE UPPER LIMB

Muscles of the upper limb are responsible for the movement of the forearm and the wrist. These will be muscles that extend from the humerus across the elbow to the ulna and/or the radius.

Triceps brachii (TRY-ceps BRAY-key-eye)

This is the only muscle on the posterior surface of the arm.

Biceps brachii

This is the most familiar muscle on the arm. It is found on the anterior surface of the arm. It is frequently a target of bodybuilders and is usually reasonably well-defined on most individuals.

Brachialis (BRAY-key-AL-us)

The brachialis can be found under the biceps brachii on the anterior surface of the humerus.

Brachioradialis (BRAY-key-oh-RAY-dee-AL-us)

This muscle is found on the lateral surface of the upper arm and extends across the elbow to insert on the radius.

Pronator teres (pro-NAY-tor TARE-eez)

This is a short muscle that runs from the humerus and ulna to the radius. It can be found opposite the brachioradialis at the elbow.

Table 1.11: Muscles of the Upper Limb

MUSCLE	ORIGIN	INSERT	ACTION
Triceps brachii	Long head – inferior margin of glenoid cavity; lateral head – posterior humerus; medial head – distal radial groove on posterior humerus	Olecranon process of ulna	Extends arm; adducts arm; extends forearm
Biceps brachii	Short head – coracoid process; Long head – superior margin of glenoid fossa	Radial tuberosity	Flexes arm; flexion of forearm; supination of hands
Brachialis	Distal portion of anterior humerus	Coronoid process of ulna	Flexion of forearm
Brachioradialis	Lateral ridge at distal end of humerus	Base of styloid process of radius	Flexion of forearm
Pronator teres	Medial epicondyle of humerus and coronoid process of ulna	Midshaft of radius	Pronate hand; flexes forearm

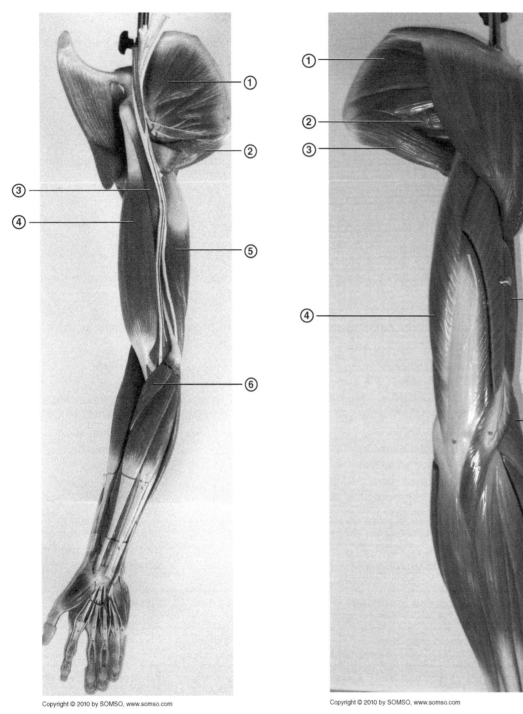

1. Subscapularis
2. Teres major
3. Coracobrachialis
4. Biceps brachii
5. Triceps brachii
6. Pronator teres

1. Infraspinatus
2. Teres minor
3. Teres major
4. Triceps brachii
5. Deltoid
6. Brachialis
7. Brachioradialis

Figure 1.45. Anterior and Posterior Muscles of the Upper Limb

SECTION E – MUSCLES OF THE PELVIS, BUTTOCKS, AND LOWER LIMB

The muscles of the pelvis, buttocks, and lower limb are responsible for movement of the thigh, leg, and foot.

Muscles of the Pelvis

Iliopsoas (ILL-ee-oh-SO-az), **Iliacus** (ILL-ee-AK-us), **Psoas major** (SO-az MAY-jor)

These muscles are the primary flexors of the thigh. They move the leg forward when walking. The iliacus and psoas major are found in the pelvic cavity and the iliopsoas is found in the proximal thigh, near the ramus of the pubis. In the upper thigh the iliacus and psoas major are essentially inseparable so they are referred to jointly as the iliopsoas.

Muscles of the Buttocks

Gluteus maximus (GLOO-te-us MAK-si-mus)

This is the largest muscle in the body. It is a surface muscle that covers a large part of the buttocks. The gluteus maximus helps straighten the leg when walking, running, and climbing stairs. It also assists in standing up from a seated position.

Gluteus medius

This muscle originates superior to, but is partially covered by, the gluteus maximus. It assists with balance during walking.

Muscles of the Thigh

Adductor magnus

This is a large triangular muscle found on the medial surface of the surface of the thigh. It can be found posterior to the gracilis.

Adductor longus

This is a triangular muscle found on the medial surface of the thigh, anterior to the gracilis.

Gracilis (grah-SIL-us)

This is a thin, straight muscle found on the medial surface of the thigh.

Sartorius (sar-TOR-ee-us)

This long narrow muscle runs obliquely across the anterior surface of the thigh.

1. Adductor magnus
2. Gracilis
3. Sartorius
4. Rectus femoris
5. Vastus medialis
6. Gastrocnemius
7. Soleus
8. Calcaneal (Achilles) tendon

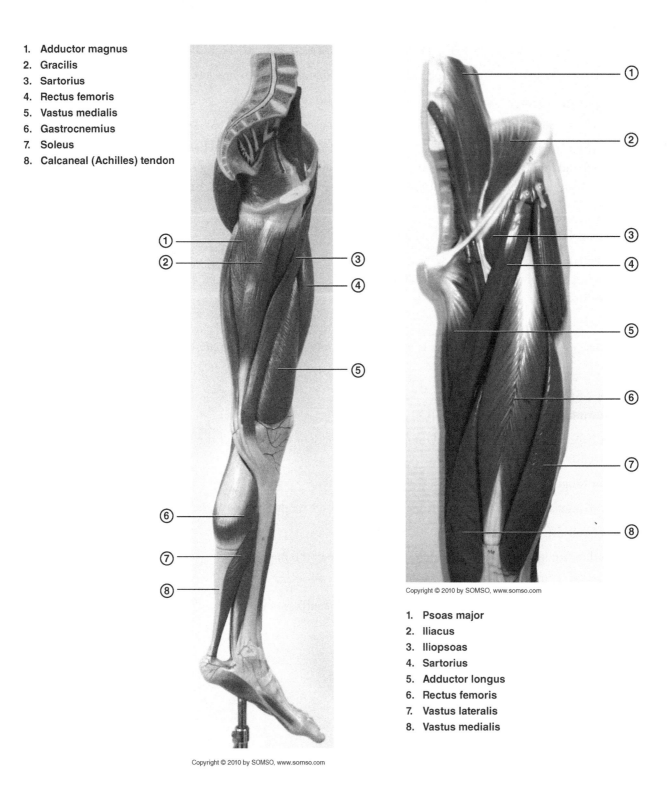

1. Psoas major
2. Iliacus
3. Iliopsoas
4. Sartorius
5. Adductor longus
6. Rectus femoris
7. Vastus lateralis
8. Vastus medialis

Figure 1.46. Muscles of the Medial Lower Limb (left), and Muscles of the Pelvis and Upper thigh (right)

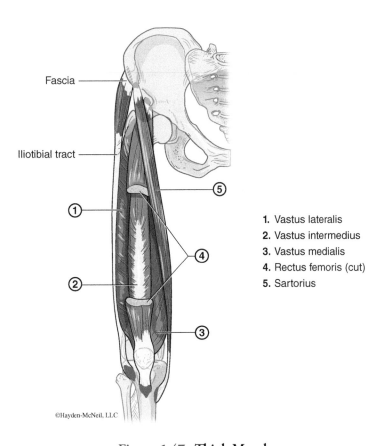

Fascia

Iliotibial tract

1. Vastus lateralis
2. Vastus intermedius
3. Vastus medialis
4. Rectus femoris (cut)
5. Sartorius

©Hayden-McNeil, LLC

Figure 1.47. Thigh Muscle

Rectus femoris (REK-tus FEE-mor-us)

This is a long straight muscle found in the center of the anterior thigh. The rectus femoris, along with the vastus lateralis, vastus medialis, and vastus intermedius are known as the quadriceps muscle. All four muscles have a common ligament, the patellar ligament, which inserts on the tibial tuberosity. However, the rectus femoris is the only one of the four that originates in the pelvis and therefore moves the thigh as well as the leg.

Vastus lateralis

This muscle is found lateral to the rectus femoris on the anterior thigh.

Vastus medialis

This muscle is found medial to the rectus femoris on the anterior thigh.

Vastus intermedius

This muscle is found beneath the rectus femoris on the anterior thigh. It is not a surface muscle.

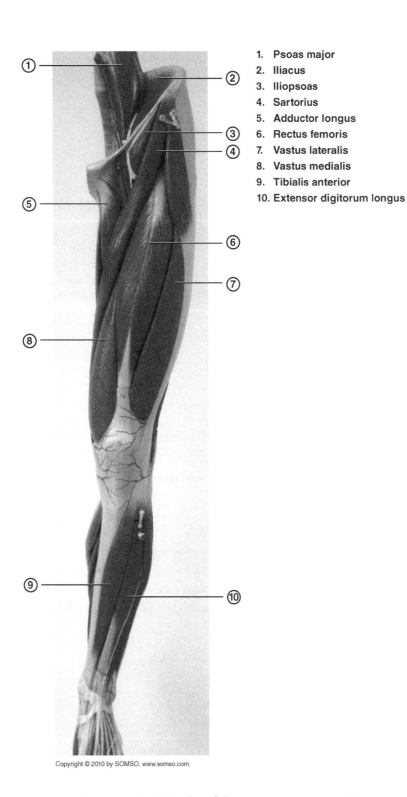

1. Psoas major
2. Iliacus
3. Iliopsoas
4. Sartorius
5. Adductor longus
6. Rectus femoris
7. Vastus lateralis
8. Vastus medialis
9. Tibialis anterior
10. Extensor digitorum longus

Figure 1.48. Muscles of the Anterior Lower Limb

Biceps femoris (BY-ceps FEE-mor-us)

This muscle is found on the lateral surface of the posterior thigh. As its name indicates it has two heads. The tendon of the biceps femoris (the hamstring) can be felt as a lateral ridge behind the knee. The biceps femoris along with the semitendinosus and the semimembranosus are known as the hamstrings.

Semitendinosus

This is a narrow muscle found on the medial surface of the posterior thigh.

Semimembranosus

This is a muscle found on the medial surface of the posterior thigh. It is wider and underneath the semitendinosus.

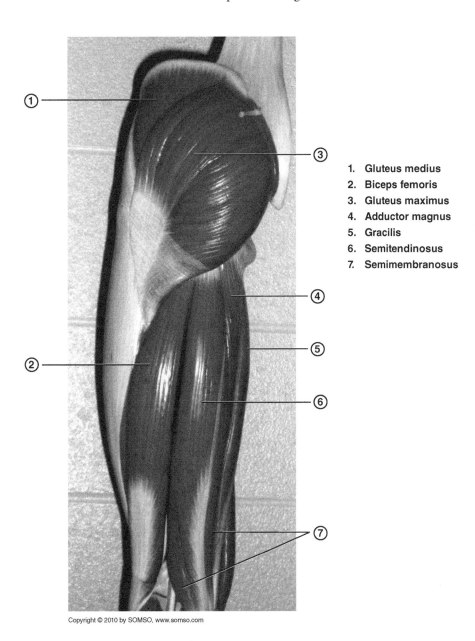

1. Gluteus medius
2. Biceps femoris
3. Gluteus maximus
4. Adductor magnus
5. Gracilis
6. Semitendinosus
7. Semimembranosus

Figure 1.49. Muscles of the Posterior Lower Limb

Muscles of the Leg
Tibialis anterior

This muscle can be found on the anterior surface of the leg. It runs parallel to the anterior margin of the tibia.

Extensor digitorum longus

This is a muscle found on the anterior surface of the leg. It is lateral to the tibialis anterior. Its main function is the extension of all the toes except the great toe.

Gastrocnemius (gas-TROW-NE-me-us)

This muscle has two prominent bellies on the posterior surface of the leg. This is the most superficial calf muscle. The gastrocnemius helps push the body forward when walking or running.

Soleus (SOW-lee-us)

This muscle is below the gastrocnemius on the posterior surface of the leg. Both the gastrocnemius and the soleus insert on the heel (calcaneus) via the calcaneal tendon, which is also known as the Achilles tendon.

Table 1.12: Muscles of Pelvis and Lower Limb

MUSCLE	ORIGIN	INSERT	ACTION
Pelvis			
Iliospoas; Iliacus; Psoas major	Iliacus – iliac fossa and crest; lateral sacrum	On and just below lesser trochanter of femur	Flexes lumbar vertebrae; flexes thigh
	Psoas major – transverse processes, bodies, and discs of T12 and lumbar vertebrae		
Buttocks			
Gluteus maximus	Dorsal ilium, sacrum, and coccyx	Gluteal tuberosity of femur and iliotibial tract	Extends, adducts, and laterally rotates thigh; braces knee
Gluteus medius	Upper lateral surface of ilium	Greater trochanter of femur	Abducts and medially rotates thigh
Medial Thigh			
Adductor magnus	Ischial and pubic rami and ischial tuberosity	Linea aspera and adductor tubercle of femur, gluteal tuberosity	Adduct, laterally rotate, flex and extend thigh
Adductor longus	Pubis near pubic symphysis	Linea aspera and middle portion of femur	Adduct, laterally rotates and flexes thigh
Gracilis	Symphysis pubis	Medial surface of tibia just inferior to medial condyle	Adducts thigh, flexes and medially rotates leg

MUSCLE	ORIGIN	INSERT	ACTION
Anterior Thigh			
Sartorius	Anterior superior iliac spine	Medial aspect of proximal tibia	Flexes and laterally rotates thigh, flexes leg
Rectus femoris	Anterior inferior iliac spine and superior margin of acetabulum	Tibial tuberosity and patella	Extends leg; flexes thigh
Vastus lateralis	Greater trochanter, intertrochanteric line and linea aspera	Tibial tuberosity and patella	Extends leg and stabilizes knee joint
Vastus medialis	Intertrochanteric line and linea aspera	Tibial tuberosity and patella	Extends leg and stabilizes knee joint
Vastus intermedius	Anterior and lateral surface of femur	Tibial tuberosity and patella	Extends leg
Posterior Thigh			
Biceps femoris	Long head – ischial tuberosity; short head – linea aspera and distal femur	Head of fibula and lateral condyle of tibia	Extends thigh; flexes leg
Semitendinosus	Ischial tuberosity	Medial aspect of upper fibula shaft	Extends thigh; flexes leg
Semimembranosus	Ischial tuberosity	Medial condyle of tibia; lateral condyle of femur	Extends thigh; flexes leg
Leg			
Tibialis anterior	Lateral condyle and upper 2/3 of tibia; interosseous membrane	Inferior surface of first cuneiform and metatarsal 1	Dorsiflexion, inverts foot
Extensor digitorum longus	Upper 2/3 of anterior shaft of fibula; interosseous membrane	Lateral four toes	Extends all toes except great toe and extends foot at ankle
Gastrocnemius	Medial and lateral condyles of femur	Calcaneus via calcaneal tendon	Flexes leg; plantarflexion foot
Soleus	Proximal portion of tibia and fibula; interosseous membrane	Calcaneus via calcaneal tendon	Plantarflexion foot

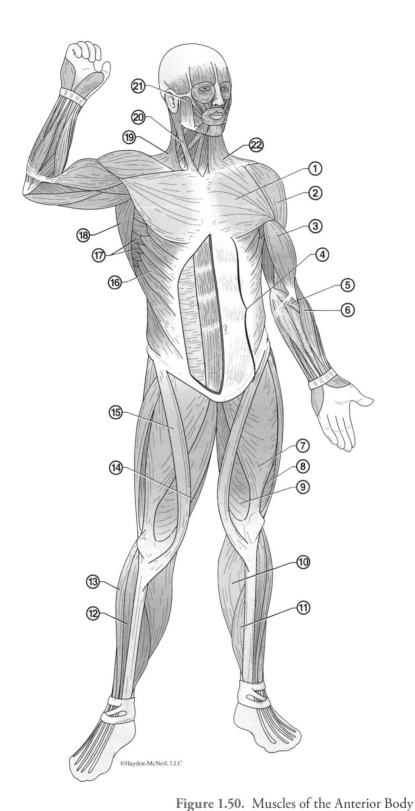

1. Pectoralis major
2. Deltoid
3. Biceps brachii
4. Rectus abdominis
5. Pronator teres
6. Brachioradialis
7. Rectus femoris
8. Vastus lateralis
9. Vastus medialis
10. Gastrocnemius
11. Soleus
12. Tibialis anterior
13. Extensor digitorum longus
14. Gracilis
15. Sartorius
16. External oblique
17. Serratus anterior
18. Latissimus dorsi
19. Trapezius
20. Sternocleidomastoid
21. Masseter
22. Platysma

©Hayden-McNeil, LLC

Figure 1.50. Muscles of the Anterior Body

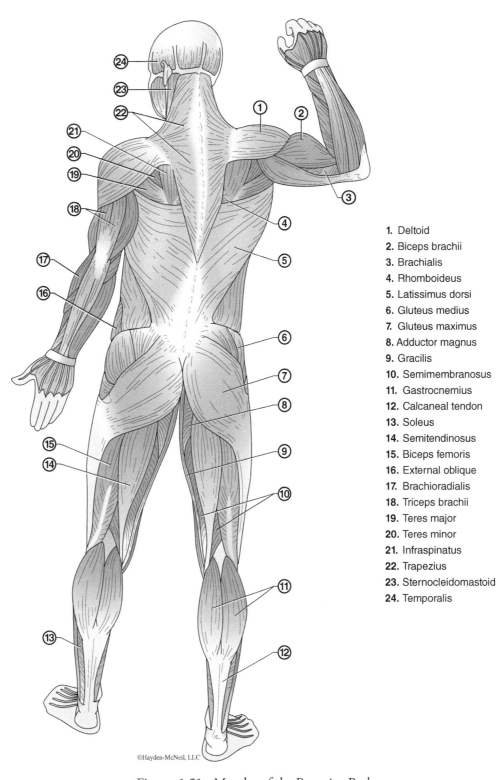

1. Deltoid
2. Biceps brachii
3. Brachialis
4. Rhomboideus
5. Latissimus dorsi
6. Gluteus medius
7. Gluteus maximus
8. Adductor magnus
9. Gracilis
10. Semimembranosus
11. Gastrocnemius
12. Calcaneal tendon
13. Soleus
14. Semitendinosus
15. Biceps femoris
16. External oblique
17. Brachioradialis
18. Triceps brachii
19. Teres major
20. Teres minor
21. Infraspinatus
22. Trapezius
23. Sternocleidomastoid
24. Temporalis

©Hayden-McNeil, LLC

Figure 1.51. Muscles of the Posterior Body

UNIT 2

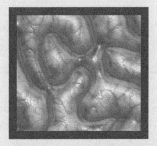

NERVOUS TISSUE, CENTRAL NERVOUS SYSTEM, SPECIAL SENSES, AND ENDOCRINE SYSTEM

PART 1

This unit will be covering the systems that allow communication in the body—the nervous system and the endocrine system. We will begin with the nervous system, then explore the ear and eye, and end this unit with the endocrine system.

NERVOUS TISSUE AND THE NEURON

Nervous tissue is one of the four types of tissues found in the human body. The primary characteristic of nervous tissue is conductivity. This tissue is capable of transmitting an impulse. This tissue is also described as irritable which means it can be stimulated. When it is stimulated it then conducts the impulse.

The fundamental unit of the nervous system is the **neuron**. This is the cell that is stimulated and responsible for transmitting nervous impulses. There are about 20 billion neurons in the cerebrum and a total of 100 billion neurons in the brain. In the spinal cord there are about 1 billion neurons. The other type of cell found in nervous tissue is the **neuroglia** or glial cells. For every neuron there are 10 to 50 glial cells. These cells serve many functions in the nervous system including support, nourishment, and protection. In the lab the only glial cell studied is the **Schwann cell** (SHWAHN) also known as a **neurolemmocyte** (NU-rah-LEM-mah-site) which is the glial cell found in the peripheral nervous system.

There are three important parts to every neuron: the **cell body**; the **dendrites** (DEN-drytes); and the **axon**. First, let's look at the cell body. This is the control center for the neuron. If the cell body dies, the neuron will die. The cell body may be called the **soma** (so-MAH) or the **perikaryon** (PER-IKER-ee-on). In the neuron you will find the same organelles as in most other cells. Neurons have a nucleus, ribosomes, Golgi bodies, mitochondria, and all the other organelles necessary for cellular function.

There are a few unique features in the cell body of a neuron that need to be addressed. Scattered throughout the cytoplasm of the neuron there are dark structures called **Nissl bodies** (NIS-ahl). These structures are mainly rough endoplasmic reticulum that are responsible for protein synthesis. The neuron has a well developed cytoskeleton that functions in support and intracellular transport. The microtubules are important in intracellular transport. There are **neurofibrils** (NU-rah-FYE-brils); very thin threads that extend into the axon to support it.

63

The dendrites are processes of the neuron that receive information from other cells or stimuli and transmit the message to the cell body. Depending on the neuron, the dendrites can take on several different appearances. These processes allow neurons to receive communications from other cells as well as monitoring the environment, internal and external.

The axon is a process that conducts the message away from the cell body toward other cells. A bundle of axons is known as a **nerve** in the peripheral nervous system, and a **tract** in the central nervous system. There is only one axon leaving a cell body, however, that axon can then branch into collaterals. At the end of the axon there are many small branches that each have a specialized **axon terminal** that ends in the **synaptic knob** (SINAP-tik). The synaptic knob contains the chemical neurotransmitter that will be released to carry the electrical message from the neuron to the next cell. The synaptic knob does not actually touch the next cell, there is a very small gap known as the **synaptic cleft**. A **synapse** is the area that encompasses the synaptic knob, synaptic cleft, and the postsynaptic membrane. Each "typical" neuron is part of a thousand to ten thousand synapses. As a result, there are about a quadrillion synapses in the brain and 60 trillion of those are just in the cerebral cortex.

Axons in the peripheral nervous system may be covered by a **myelin sheath** (MY-ah-lin) formed by neurolemmocytes (Schwann cells). Myelin is a fatty material that serves as insulation on the axon. It is also responsible for the white color of white matter in the nervous system. The neurolemmocytes are wrapped around the axon and the myelin is found between this cell and the axon of the neuron. The nucleus and organelles of the neurolemmocyte are found just beneath the neurilemma. The membranous sheath of the neurolemmocyte around the axon is the **neurilemma** (alternate spelling: neurolemma). There are several neurolemmocytes (Schwann cells) covering each axon and the gaps between these cells are the **nodes of Ranvier** (RON-vee-ay), or **neurofibril nodes**.

Neurons can be classified according to their functions. **Sensory** or **afferent neurons** transmit impulses from sensory receptors to the central nervous system. **Motor** or **efferent neurons** transmit impulses from the central nervous system to the muscles or glands. **Interneurons** are found only in the central nervous system where they connect neuron to neuron.

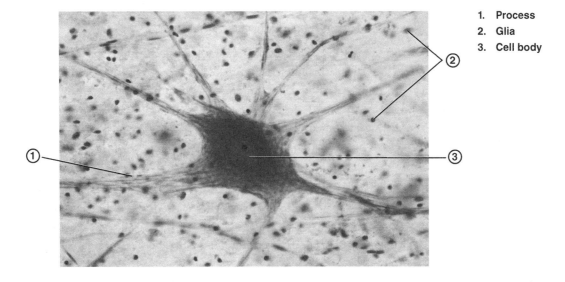

1. Process
2. Glia
3. Cell body

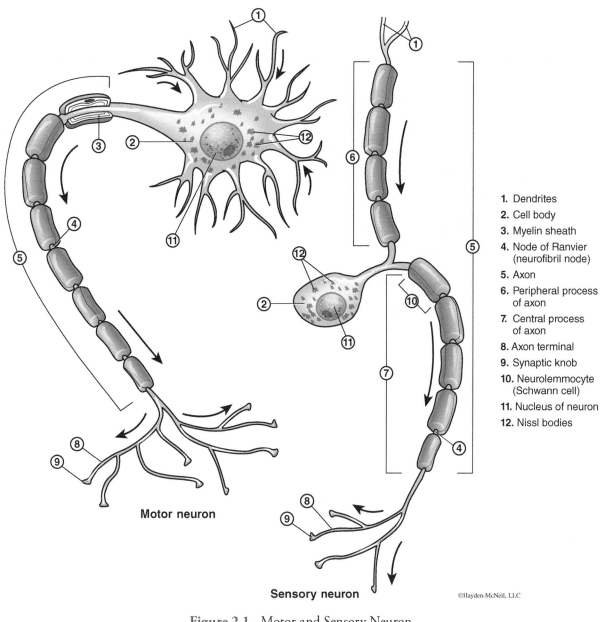

1. Dendrites
2. Cell body
3. Myelin sheath
4. Node of Ranvier (neurofibril node)
5. Axon
6. Peripheral process of axon
7. Central process of axon
8. Axon terminal
9. Synaptic knob
10. Neurolemmocyte (Schwann cell)
11. Nucleus of neuron
12. Nissl bodies

Motor neuron

Sensory neuron

©Hayden-McNeil, LLC

Figure 2.1. Motor and Sensory Neuron

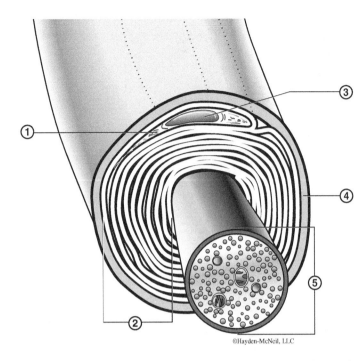

1. Cell body of neurolemmocyte (Schwann cell)
2. Myelin sheath
3. Nucleus of neurolemmocyte (Schwann cell)
4. Neurilemma
5. Axon

©Hayden-McNeil, LLC

Figure 2.2. Axon with Myelin Sheath

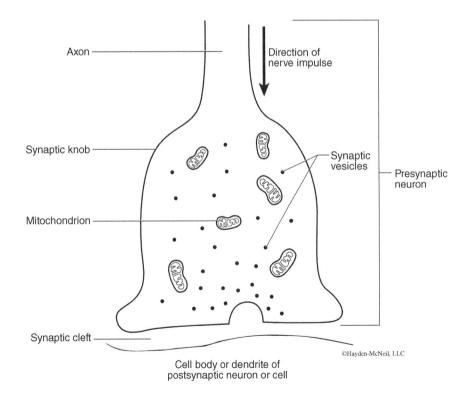

©Hayden-McNeil, LLC

Figure 2.3. Synaptic Knob

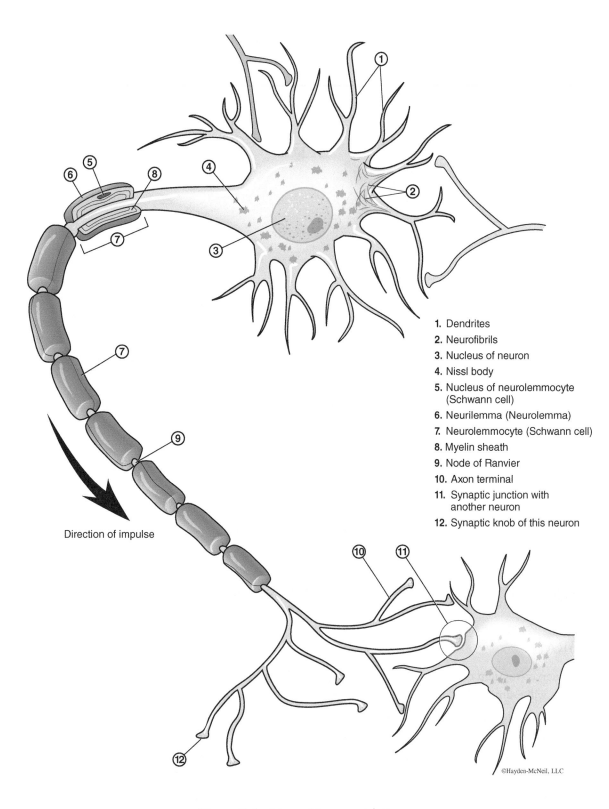

1. Dendrites
2. Neurofibrils
3. Nucleus of neuron
4. Nissl body
5. Nucleus of neurolemmocyte (Schwann cell)
6. Neurilemma (Neurolemma)
7. Neurolemmocyte (Schwann cell)
8. Myelin sheath
9. Node of Ranvier
10. Axon terminal
11. Synaptic junction with another neuron
12. Synaptic knob of this neuron

Direction of impulse

©Hayden-McNeil, LLC

Figure 2.4. Motor Neuron with Synapse

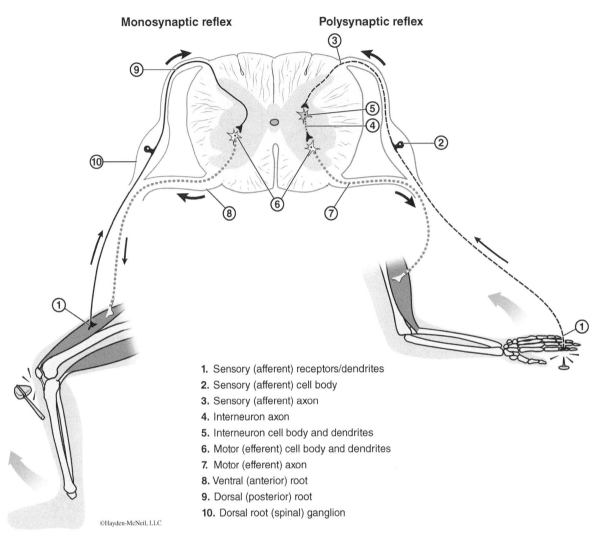

Monosynaptic reflex **Polysynaptic reflex**

1. Sensory (afferent) receptors/dendrites
2. Sensory (afferent) cell body
3. Sensory (afferent) axon
4. Interneuron axon
5. Interneuron cell body and dendrites
6. Motor (efferent) cell body and dendrites
7. Motor (efferent) axon
8. Ventral (anterior) root
9. Dorsal (posterior) root
10. Dorsal root (spinal) ganglion

©Hayden-McNeil, LLC

Figure 2.5. Spinal Cross Section with Neurons

PART 2

THE BRAIN

The central nervous system consists of the brain and the spinal cord. You will first examine the brain and then in the next part you will examine the spinal cord.

The human brain weighs about three pounds and is located inside the skull or cranium which protects it from harm. The brain is made of white and gray matter. White matter refers to the presence of myelin and gray matter refers to the absence of myelin. When observing actual brain tissue it does not actually appear gray and white. All brain tissue appears beige with the gray matter referring to the darker beige tissue and the white matter referring to the lighter beige tissue.

In the cerebrum and cerebellum the gray matter is a thin layer on the exterior surface and is referred to as the cortex. The white matter is located in the interior. The thalamus and hypothalamus are mainly gray matter. In the brainstem gray matter is scattered within the white matter and is associated with the reflex centers.

The brain has four main divisions: the **cerebrum** (SER-e-brum), the **diencephalon** (DYE-en-SEF-ah-lon), the **cerebellum** (ser-e-BELL-um), and the **brainstem**. The brainstem is the most inferior part of the brain and it consists of the **medulla oblongata** (mah-DUL-ah OB-long-GAH-tah), **pons** (PONZ), and **midbrain**. The brainstem is the structure that connects the brain with the spinal cord. Attached posteriorly to the pons and midbrain is the cerebellum. Superior to the brainstem is the diencephalon, and the largest division of the brain is the cerebrum.

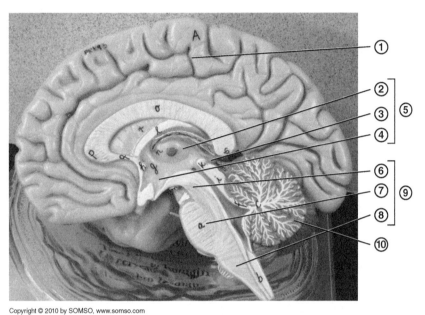

1. Cerebrum
2. Thalamus
3. Pineal gland/body
4. Hypothalamus
5. Diencephalon
6. Midbrain
7. Pons
8. Medulla oblongata
9. Brainstem
10. Cerebellum

Copyright © 2010 by SOMSO, www.somso.com

Figure 2.6. Divisions of the Brain

Cerebrum

The **cerebrum** has two hemispheres that superficially appear the same. The surface of the cerebrum has many ridges and grooves. The ridges are the **gyri** (JI-rye) [singular, gyrus (JI-rahs)] and the grooves are the **sulci** (SUL-key) [singular, sulcus (SUL-kus)]. Deep grooves are called **fissures**. The fissures, sulci, and gyri are used as markers to identify locations or separate areas of the brain.

Each hemisphere consists of five lobes. However, only four of the lobes are visible on the surface of the brain. The frontal lobe is located beneath the frontal bone; the parietal lobe is beneath the parietal bone; the temporal lobe below the temporal bone, and the occipital lobe below the occipital bone. The fifth lobe is located by separating the lateral fissure between the frontal lobe and temporal lobe. This is the insula and is not visible anywhere in the laboratory.

The **frontal lobe** is located anterior to the **central sulcus**. The somatic motor cortex is found in the **precentral gyrus** of this lobe. The prefrontal areas are involved in emotions, motivation, and personality.

The **parietal lobe** is located posterior to the central sulcus. The **postcentral gyrus** in this lobe is the location of the somatic sensory cortex. The area behind the postcentral gyrus is involved in visual-spatial relationships and proprioception, which is the awareness of the position of body parts in space.

The **temporal lobe** is separated from the frontal lobe by the **lateral fissure**. This lobe contains the auditory cortex which is concerned with hearing. It also plays an important role in memory, language, and speech.

The **occipital lobe** is located in the posterior region of the brain. This lobe is primarily concerned with vision as it is the location of the visual cortex.

The **insula** is located under the lateral fissure of the brain and is not visible in lab. This lobe plays a role in some language functions as well as processes certain sensory input such as pain, temperature sensation, and possibly taste. It also integrates sensory and autonomic information from the viscera.

The crevice between the two hemispheres is the **longitudinal fissure**. The crevice between the cerebrum and the cerebellum is the **transverse fissure**. The **central sulcus** is the groove that separates the frontal and parietal lobes. The **lateral fissure** is the crevice between the frontal and temporal lobes.

Most structures that must be identified in the brain can be located by viewing the sagittal or inferior view. On the sagittal section there is a wide curved band of white fibrous tissue; this is the **corpus callosum** (KOR-pus kah-LO-sum). It is a band of commissural fibers that allows communication between the two hemispheres. This structure actually contains about 250 million fibers. When you dissect the sheep's brain you will be cutting through this structure.

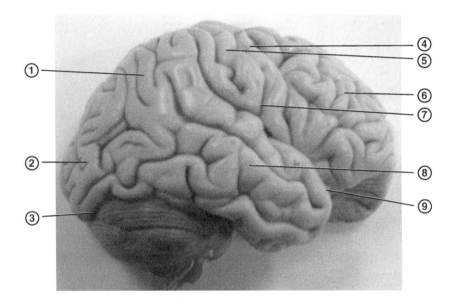

1. Parietal lobe
2. Occipital lobe
3. Transverse fissure
4. Precentral gyrus
5. Postcentral gyrus
6. Frontal lobe
7. Central sulcus
8. Temporal lobe
9. Lateral fissure

Figure 2.7. Lobes, Gyri, and Fissures of the Cerebrum

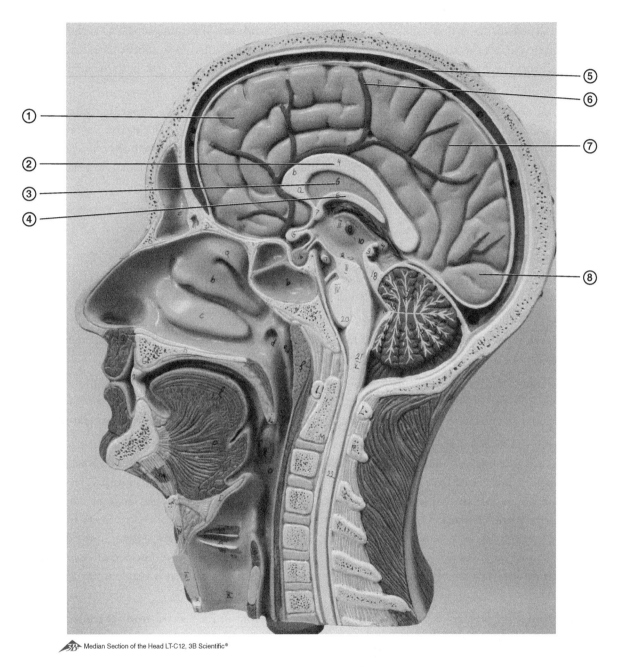

3B Median Section of the Head LT-C12, 3B Scientific®

1. Frontal lobe	4. Fornix	7. Parietal lobe
2. Corpus callosum	5. Superior sagittal sinus	8. Occipital lobe
3. Septum pellucidum	6. Central sulcus	

Figure 2.8. Structures of the Cerebrum

Below and attached to the corpus callosum is the **septum pellucidum** (SEP-tum pah-LOO-si-dum). This is a membrane that separates the lateral ventricles of the brain. Below this structure is another band of nerve fibers known as the **fornix** (FOR-niks). This connects the hippocampus, part of the limbic system, to the mamillary bodies of the hypothalamus.

Surrounding the outer perimeter of the cerebrum is a large vein-like structure called the **superior sagittal sinus**. This venous vessel collects the blood from the veins that drain the cerebral hemispheres. This is just one of a number of venous vessels known as the dural sinuses that drain the brain. Ultimately they drain into the internal jugular vein to return oxygen poor blood to the heart. The superior sagittal sinus is the location of the arachnoid granulations that return cerebrospinal fluid to the venous blood.

On the inferior surface of the cerebrum are the **olfactory bulbs** and **olfactory tracts**. These structures carry the sense of smell from the olfactory nerves in the roof of the nose to the brain.

Diencephalon

Located inferior to the cerebrum is the diencephalon. The thalamus, hypothalamus, optic chiasma, pituitary gland, and the pineal gland are all located in this division of the brain.

The **thalamus** (THAL-ah-mus) is located just below the fornix. The tissue of the thalamus makes up the walls of the third ventricle. In the center of this area there is the **intermediate mass of the thalamus**, which connects the two lobes of the thalamus. This area of the brain serves as a sensory relay station.

The **hypothalamus** (HY-po-TAL-ah-mus) is located below the thalamus and the tissue makes up the floor of the third ventricle. This area of the brain has an immense impact on life. It essentially regulates homeostasis. It controls the pituitary gland and actually produces two of the hormones released by the posterior pituitary gland.

The **hypophysis** (hi-POF-i-sis), which is also known as the **pituitary gland**, is situated below the hypothalamus and connected to it by the **infundibulum** (in-fun-DIB-u-lum). The infundibulum is a hollow stalk that serves as a passageway for hormones and regulatory factors. Two projections off the hypothalamus just posterior to the hypophysis are the **mamillary bodies** (MAM-ah-LAR-e). These serve as olfactory relay stations. Anterior to the hypophysis is the **optic chiasma** (OP-tik ki-AZ-mah). This is the point where optic nerve fibers from the nasal portion of each retina cross over to the opposite side of the brain. The **optic nerves** are anterior to the optic chiasma while the **optic tracts** are posterior. Chiasma means to cross over or form an X. When observed on the inferior brain the optic chiasma does have the appearance of an X. On the sagittal section, all that is visible is the center of the X so it appears as an oval structure.

The **pineal gland** (PIN-e-al) or body and the **choroid plexus** (KO-roid PLEK-sus) **of third ventricle** are structures of the epithalamus, which forms the roof of the third ventricle. The pineal gland is a neuroendocrine structure. It is stimulated by the nervous system and releases a hormone, melatonin. This gland can be found at the end of the choroid plexus of the third ventricle and slightly superior and posterior to the corpora quadrigemina of the midbrain. The choroid plexus is a structure found in the roof of every ventricle and is composed of a capillary bed, pia mater, and ependymal cells. It produces the cerebrospinal fluid (CSF) that is found in the ventricles of the brain, the subarachnoid space, and central canal of the spinal cord.

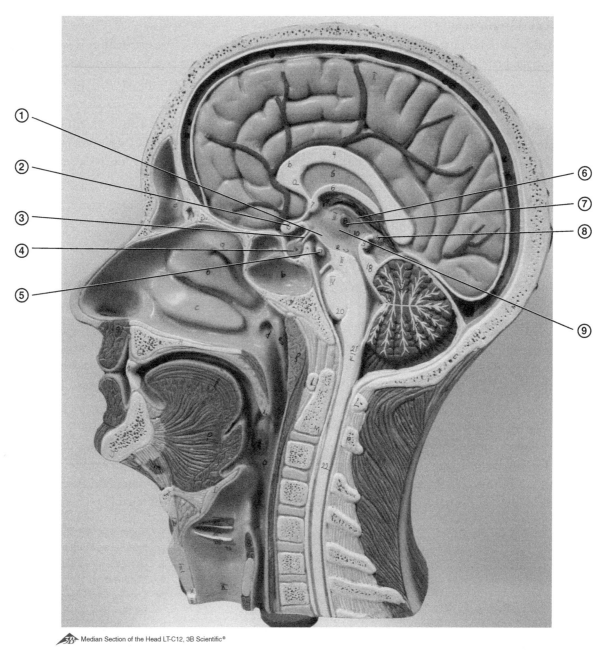

Median Section of the Head LT-C12, 3B Scientific®

1. Hypothalamus	4. Pituitary gland (hypophysis)	7. Intermediate mass of thalamus
2. Optic Chiasma	5. Mamillary body	8. Pineal gland (body)
3. Infundibulum	6. Choroid plexus of 3rd ventricle	9. Thalamus (tissue) 3rd ventricle (space)

Figure 2.9. Structures of the Diencephalon

Cerebellum and Brainstem

The most inferior divisions of the brain are the cerebellum and the brainstem. The **cerebellum** is located on the dorsal aspect of the brain inferior to the occipital lobe of the cerebrum and posterior to the pons and midbrain. It is responsible for muscle coordination, posture, and balance. It consists of two hemispheres with gyri and sulci on the surface.

Anterior to the cerebellum is the **brainstem**. The most superior division of the brainstem is the **midbrain** or the **mesencephalon** (mez-en-SEF-a-lon). Below the midbrain is the **pons** and the most inferior portion is the **medulla oblongata**. As the nervous tissue from the medulla oblongata narrows and passes through the foramen magnum of the skull it becomes the spinal cord.

The midbrain contains a couple of important structures. On the sagittal section of the brainstem, it appears that the midbrain is dissected by a canal. This is the **cerebral aqueduct** (SUREE-bral AH-kwah-duct) or the **cerebral aqueduct of Sylvius** that connects the third ventricle with the **fourth ventricle**.

Posterior to the cerebral aqueduct there are two pairs of rounded processes. These four masses are known as the **corpora quadrigemina** (KOR-pour-ah KWAH-dri-JEM-i-nah). The two superior masses are the **superior colliculi** (ko-LIK-you-lye) (singular: colliculus) which are involved in visual reflexes. The two inferior masses are the **inferior colliculi** which are involved in auditory reflexes.

The **pons** is the rounded bulge of the brainstem below the midbrain. It serves to relay impulses between the medulla and the cerebrum as well as between the cerebrum and the cerebellum. It also contains reflex centers involved in inspiration (inhalation). Between the pons and the cerebellum there is a triangular cavity known as the fourth ventricle.

Between the pons and the foramen magnum is the **medulla oblongata**. It is a slightly enlarged continuation of the spinal cord. It contains several reflex centers, most importantly the reflex centers for heart rate, blood pressure, and respiration. The dorsal surface forms the floor of the fourth ventricle. The **pyramids** are a pair of elevations on the anterior surface of the medulla. Tracts entering and leaving the brain may pass through these structures and will be called pyramidal tracts. If the tracts pass around the pyramids they are extrapyramidal tracts.

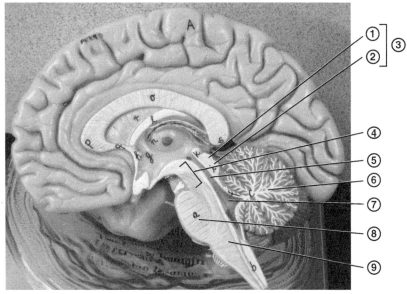

1. Superior colliculus
2. Inferior colliculus
3. Corpora quadrigemina
4. Midbrain
5. Cerebral aqueduct (of Sylvius)
6. Cerebellum
7. Fourth (4th) ventricle
8. Pons
9. Medulla

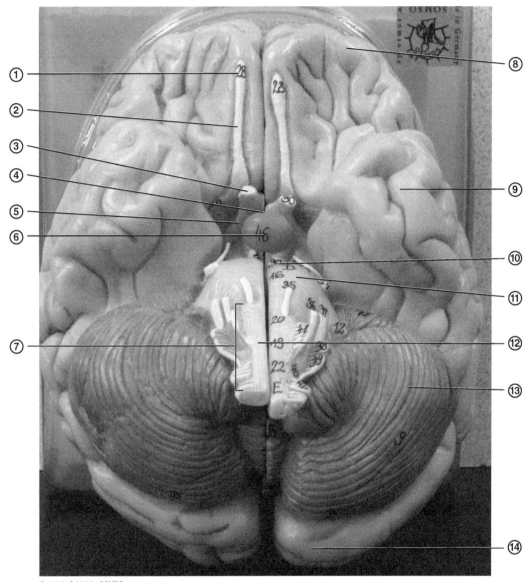

1. Olfactory bulb
2. Olfactory tract
3. Optic nerve
4. Optic chiasma
5. Optic tract
6. Pituitary gland (hypophysis)
7. Medulla oblongata
8. Frontal lobe
9. Temporal lobe
10. Mamillary body
11. Pons
12. Pyramid
13. Cerebellum
14. Occipital lobe

Figure 2.10. Inferior Brain

Meninges

It is apparent that the brain and spinal cord are important. They are also delicate tissue. The skull provides a rigid protective case for the brain, and the vertebral column provides protection for the spinal cord. However, there are additional structures that are involved in the protection of the brain and spinal cord. Both the meninges and the cerebrospinal fluid aid in the protection of the brain. The meninges will be discussed first.

The **meninges** (meh-NIN-jes) are three layers of tissue that cover the brain and spinal cord—**dura mater** (DOO-rah MAY-ter), **arachnoid mater** (ah-RAK-noyd), and **pia mater** (PI-ah). The dura mater is the outermost layer. It is tough, white, dense connective tissue that contains blood vessels and nerves. It is the most durable of the meninges. In the skull it is attached to the inner surface of the bones and forms the internal periosteum, so there is no space between the dura mater and the skull bones.

Between the hemispheres of the cerebrum and cerebellum as well as between the cerebrum and cerebellum it extends inward to form partitions known as the **falx cerebri** (FALKS SER-ah-bri), **falx cerebelli** (ser-ah-BELL-i), and **tentorium cerebelli** (ten-TOE-ree-um). In some areas there are canals in the dura mater that contain venous blood, these are the dural sinuses.

The dura mater continues to cover the spinal cord. However, in the vertebral column it is not fused with the bones. This results in the space containing blood vessels and adipose tissue between the dura mater and the periosteum of the vertebrae. This space is the **epidural space**. The name refers to the fact that the space is on or above the dura mater. It is only present in the spinal cord, not in the brain. This space has a purpose in anesthesia. It can be used to administer anesthetics to block pain sensations.

The dura mater covering the spinal cord continues to the level of the second sacral vertebra, well beyond the end of the spinal cord. The dura mater and the pia mater continue beyond this point as a filament to secure the spinal cord at the end of the spinal canal. This is the **filum terminale** (FI-lum TER-min-NAL-ee). The pia mater and the dura mater also fuse together in places along the length of the spinal cord to form the **denticulate ligament** (den-TIK-you-late) which secures the spinal cord in the center of the spinal canal.

The second layer of the meninges is the arachnoid mater or sometimes known simply as the arachnoid. This is a thin membrane that has the appearance of a spider web, hence the name. It is located between the dura mater and pia mater. It does not follow the contour of the brain and spinal cord but it does have thin strands that extend from it and attaches to the pia mater. There are also projections of the arachnoid mater through the dura mater into the dural sinuses. These projections are the **arachnoid granulations** that consist of a number of arachnoid villi. These structures function to return cerebrospinal fluid to the venous blood.

Normally the arachnoid mater is pressed against the inner surface of the dura mater by cerebrospinal fluid pressure in the subarachnoid space. However, there is the potential for fluid to collect in the space between these two layers. This potential space is the **subdural space**, referring to the fact it would be located below the dura mater. In normal individuals there is no space, however, if there is damage to the dural sinuses it is possible for blood to collect in this space to cause a subdural hematoma.

The pia mater is the innermost meninges. It is a very thin membrane that contains blood vessels and nerves. It lies on the surface of the brain and spinal cord, following the contours. As mentioned earlier the pia mater along with the dura mater forms the denticulate ligament and the filum terminale.

Between the arachnoid mater and the pia mater there is a fluid-filled space that is the **subarachnoid space**. The fluid is the cerebrospinal fluid (CSF).

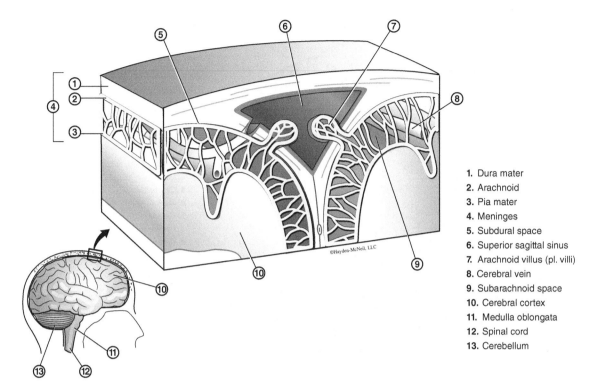

1. Dura mater
2. Arachnoid
3. Pia mater
4. Meninges
5. Subdural space
6. Superior sagittal sinus
7. Arachnoid villus (pl. villi)
8. Cerebral vein
9. Subarachnoid space
10. Cerebral cortex
11. Medulla oblongata
12. Spinal cord
13. Cerebellum

©Hayden-McNeil, LLC

Figure 2.11. Meninges of the Brain

Ventricles

The **ventricles** are four fluid-filled cavities located in the cerebrum, diencephalon, and brainstem. The fluid found in the ventricles is cerebrospinal fluid (CSF). In the cerebrum there are two **lateral ventricles**, one in each hemisphere. These ventricles are connected by way of the **interventricular foramina** with the **third ventricle**, which can be found in the midline region of the diencephalon, between the two hemispheres. The thalamus makes up the walls of the third ventricle, while the floor is made up of the hypothalamus, and the epithalamus makes up the roof. The third ventricle is connected to the **fourth ventricle** by way of the cerebral aqueduct.

The cerebrospinal fluid is formed in the choroid plexuses of the ventricles. A choroid plexus is a specialized capillary bed located in the roof of each ventricle. Each plexus secretes CSF; however, the majority of the fluid is produced in the lateral ventricles.

Cerebrospinal Fluid

Cerebrospinal fluid is another protective factor for the central nervous system. The fluid serves as a shock absorber as well as a method for the brain to monitor conditions within the body. After the CSF is formed in the choroid plexuses it flows through the ventricles. The fluid in lateral ventricles flows through the interventricular foramina into the third ventricle. The fluid then flows through the cerebral aqueduct to the fourth ventricle. From the fourth ventricle the fluid flows into the central canal of the spinal cord which is continuous with the fourth ventricle. The CSF also enters the subarachnoid space through the 2 lateral aperatures in the walls and the single medial aperature in the roof of the fourth ventricle. After passing through the subarachnoid space the CSF is reabsorbed into the blood by way of the **arachnoid granulations**, which penetrate the dura mater into the superior sagittal sinus. This allows the cerebrospinal fluid to be replaced on a regular basis, usually about every 8 hours. There is 125 to 150 mL of CSF in the central nervous system. The body produces about 400–500 mL each day. The CSF also produces a pressure that can be measured during a lumbar puncture or by way of an intracranial pressure transducer. The normal pressure of the CSF is 70–180 mm H_2O.

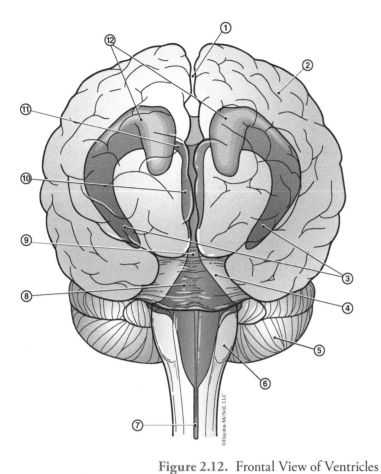

Figure 2.12. Frontal View of Ventricles

1. Longitudinal fissure
2. Cerebrum
3. Inferior horns of lateral ventricle
4. Pons
5. Cerebellum
6. Medulla oblongata
7. Central canal of spinal cord
8. Fourth ventricle
9. Cerebral aqueduct (aqueduct of Sylvius)
10. Third ventricle
11. Interventricular foramen
12. Lateral ventricles

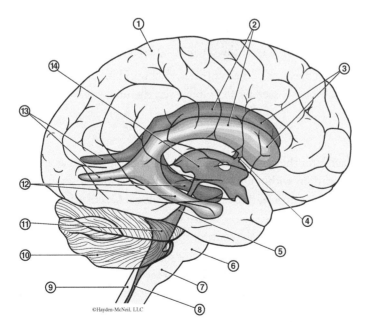

Figure 2.13. Lateral View of Ventricles

1. Cerebral hemisphere
2. Lateral ventricles
3. Anterior horns of lateral ventricles
4. Interventricular foramen
5. Cerebral aqueduct (aqueduct of Sylvius)
6. Pons
7. Medulla oblongata
8. Central canal of spinal cord
9. Spinal cord
10. Cerebellum
11. Fourth ventricle
12. Inferior horns of lateral ventricles
13. Posterior horns of lateral ventricles
14. Third ventricle

Sheep Brain Dissection

To assist in your understanding of the brain you will be dissecting a sheep's brain. You will need a preserved sheep's brain with the dura mater, a dissecting tray, a scalpel, scissors, and a probe. Remove the brain from the container. It will be covered with the dura mater. Carefully look over the brain and identify the pituitary gland on the inferior surface. You will note that the dura mater covers this structure. When you remove the dura mater you want to cut it around the pituitary so that you do not remove it with the dura mater.

Carefully remove the dura mater. Note how strong and durable it is. Fused with the dura mater is the arachnoid mater, and therefore, you will not be able to see it. You will note that the dura and arachnoid mater are not attached to the surface of the brain; this is due to the presence of the subarachnoid space. The pia mater adheres to the surface of the brain and will give the brain a glistening appearance. Carefully remove the falx cerebri and the tentorium cerebelli.

Before you perform a sagittal section on the brain, if you gently pull down on the cerebellum you will be able to visualize the corpora quadrigemina. Slightly superior to this structure you should be able to visualize the pineal gland. Turn the brain over and find the olfactory bulbs. Compare the sizes of the sheep's and the human's olfactory bulb.

You will now perform a sagittal section on the sheep's brain. Using the scalpel cut down from the superior surface through the longitudinal fissure. Cut the brain completely in half. You should now be able to identify the major structures of the sheep's brain that are visible on sagittal section. Your lab objectives have a list of structures you should be able to identify on the sheep's brain.

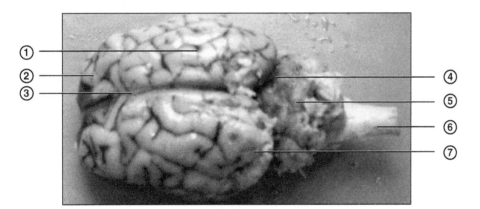

1. Parietal lobe
2. Frontal lobe
3. Longitudinal fissure
4. Transverse fissure
5. Cerebellum
6. Brainstem
7. Occipital lobe

Figure 2.14. Superior View of Sheep's Brain

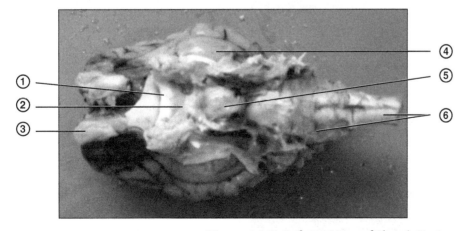

1. Optic nerve
2. Optic chiasma
3. Olfactory bulb
4. Temporal lobe
5. Hypophysis/pituitary gland
6. Brainstem

Figure 2.15. Inferior View of Sheep's Brain

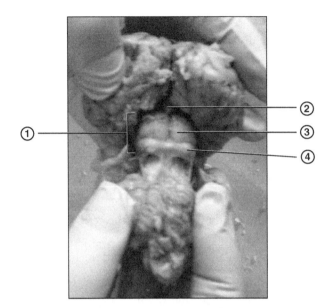

1. Corpora quadrigemina
2. Pineal gland/body
3. Superior colliculus
4. Inferior colliculus

Figure 2.16. Posterior View of Sheep's Brain

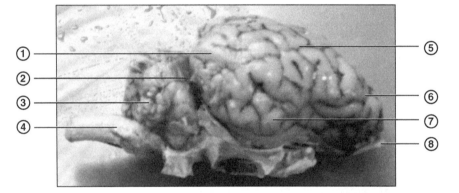

1. Occipital lobe
2. Transverse fissure
3. Cerebellum
4. Brainstem
5. Parietal lobe
6. Frontal lobe
7. Temporal lobe
8. Olfactory bulb

Figure 2.17. Lateral View of Sheep's Brain

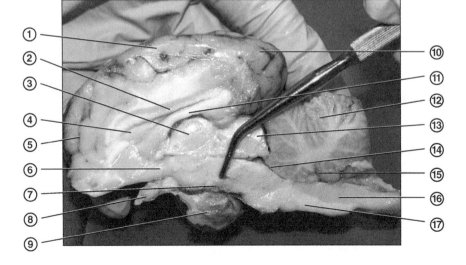

1. Parietal lobe
2. Corpus callosum
3. Space—3rd ventricle
   Tissue—thalamus
4. Septum pellucidum
5. Frontal lobe
6. Hypothalamus
7. Mamillary body
8. Optic chiasma
9. Pituitary/hypophysis
10. Occipital lobe
11. Fornix
12. Cerebellum
13. Corpora quadrigemina
14. Cerebral aqueduct
15. 4th ventricle
16. Medulla
17. Pons

Figure 2.18. Mid-Sagittal View of Sheep's Brain

PART 3

THE SPINAL CORD, SOMATIC REFLEX ARC, VISCERAL REFLEX ARC

The central nervous system continues outside the cranium as the spinal cord. This structure weighs about 1.25 ounces, has a diameter at its widest point of about 1.5 inches and has a length of about 17–18 inches. It is not a very large structure, but it serves as a conduit between the brain and the body. The spinal cord extends from the foramen magnum to between the first and second lumbar vertebrae. It does not fill the entire vertebral column, which measures about 27.5 inches. After the spinal cord terminates at the **conus medullaris** the nerves exit the cord and stay within the spinal foramen of the vertebral column until they exit at the appropriate level. This mass of nerves within the vertebral column is the **cauda equina** (KAW-do ee-KWAY-nah).

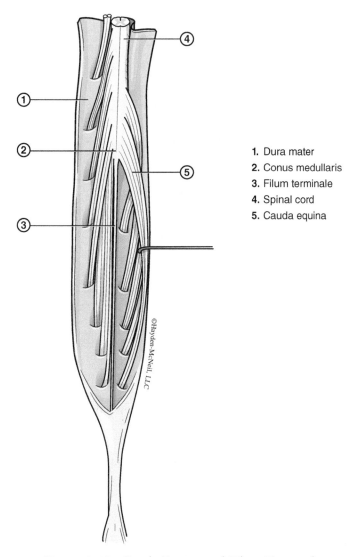

1. Dura mater
2. Conus medullaris
3. Filum terminale
4. Spinal cord
5. Cauda equina

©Hayden-McNeil, LLC

Figure 2.19. Cauda Equina and Filum Terminale

The spinal cord is protected by a bony covering, the vertebral column, a membranous covering, the meninges, and is surrounded by fluid, the cerebrospinal fluid, just like the brain. It is important to protect the delicate spinal cord just as the brain is protected. The spinal cord is also secured within the spinal canal by extensions of the dura mater and pia mater. The spinal cord is secured to the bottom of the spinal canal by the **filum terminale** and is secured at the sides by the **denticulate ligament**.

The spinal cord is covered by the three layers of meninges like the brain. However, in the spinal cord there is a space between the dura mater and the periosteum of the vertebrae, so in the spinal column there is an **epidural space**, unlike the brain.

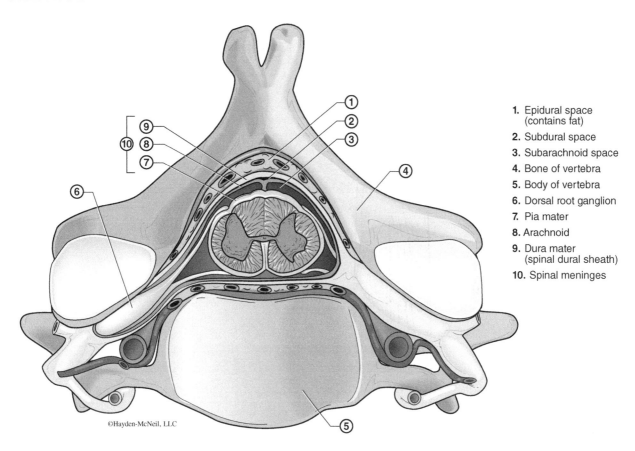

1. Epidural space (contains fat)
2. Subdural space
3. Subarachnoid space
4. Bone of vertebra
5. Body of vertebra
6. Dorsal root ganglion
7. Pia mater
8. Arachnoid
9. Dura mater (spinal dural sheath)
10. Spinal meninges

©Hayden-McNeil, LLC

Figure 2.20. Meninges of the Spinal Cord

White myelinated fibers and gray cell bodies are found in the spinal cord. In this structure the white fibers, or nerve tracts, are on the exterior and the gray matter, or the cell bodies, are in the center of the spinal cord. The pattern the gray matter creates is described as a butterfly or an H-shape. In the midline it is divided by an **anterior median fissure** and a **posterior median sulcus**. The anterior fissure is deeper than the posterior sulcus so this characteristic can be used to determine the orientation of the spinal cord.

In the center of the spinal cord is the **central canal**. This is an extension of the fourth ventricle and contains cerebrospinal fluid. This fluid returns to the brain via the subarachnoid space between the arachnoid mater and pia mater in the spinal meninges.

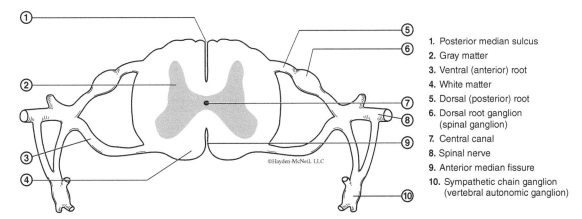

1. Posterior median sulcus
2. Gray matter
3. Ventral (anterior) root
4. White matter
5. Dorsal (posterior) root
6. Dorsal root ganglion (spinal ganglion)
7. Central canal
8. Spinal nerve
9. Anterior median fissure
10. Sympathetic chain ganglion (vertebral autonomic ganglion)

Figure 2.21. Transverse View of Spinal Cord without Vertebrae

Entering and exiting the ventral and dorsal spinal cord are nerve roots. The motor or efferent fibers exit the spinal cord via the **ventral nerve roots**. The sensory or afferent fibers enter the spinal cord by way of the **dorsal nerve roots**. On the dorsal nerve root you will notice an enlargement which contains the cell body for the sensory neuron. This is the **dorsal root** or **spinal ganglion** (plural, ganglia). A short distance outside the spinal cord, the ventral and dorsal nerve roots join to form a spinal nerve. There are 31 pairs of spinal nerves that exit the spinal cord and the vertebral column by way of the intervertebral foramina, except for the first nerve. The first spinal nerve exits between the skull and the atlas.

1. Posterior median sulcus
2. Pia mater
3. Central canal
4. White matter
5. Dorsal roots
6. Ventral roots
7. Dorsal root ganglion (spinal ganglion)
8. Spinal nerve
9. Epidural space
10. Subarachnoid space
11. Dorsal horn of gray matter
12. Ventral horn of gray matter
13. Denticulate ligament
14. Sympathetic chain ganglion (vertebral autonomic ganglion)
15. Anterior median fissure

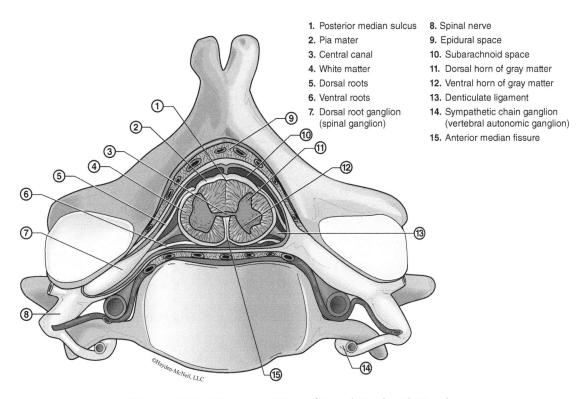

Figure 2.22. Transverse View of Spinal Cord with Vertebra

Somatic Reflex Arc

A reflex is a motor response to a stimulus without conscious thought. For example, when you touch something sharp you pull away from it. The pathway that the impulses follow to cause the motor response to a stimulus is called a reflex arc.

All reflex arcs have the following components:

1. A **receptor** which is the structure that is being stimulated.

2. A **sensory** or **afferent neuron** which carries the stimulus to the central nervous system.

3. An integration center which could be the brain or the spinal cord.

4. A **motor** or **efferent neuron** which carries the impulse for the response away from the central nervous system.

5. An **effector** or muscle which is responsible for the motor response.

If the effector is a skeletal muscle the reflex is called a somatic reflex. There are many different somatic reflexes, such as pulling away from pain or heat. Physicians use reflexes as an assessment tool for the condition of the nervous system.

At the minimum, a reflex arc requires two neurons: an afferent or sensory neuron and an efferent or motor neuron. In this situation the afferent neuron synapses with the efferent neuron in the central nervous system. However, frequently there is a third neuron located entirely in the central nervous system which is the **interneuron**. This additional neuron is situated between the afferent and efferent neurons.

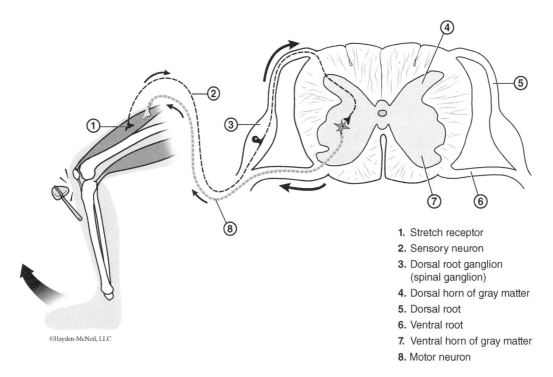

©Hayden-McNeil, LLC

1. Stretch receptor
2. Sensory neuron
3. Dorsal root ganglion (spinal ganglion)
4. Dorsal horn of gray matter
5. Dorsal root
6. Ventral root
7. Ventral horn of gray matter
8. Motor neuron

Figure 2.23. Two Neuron Reflex Arc

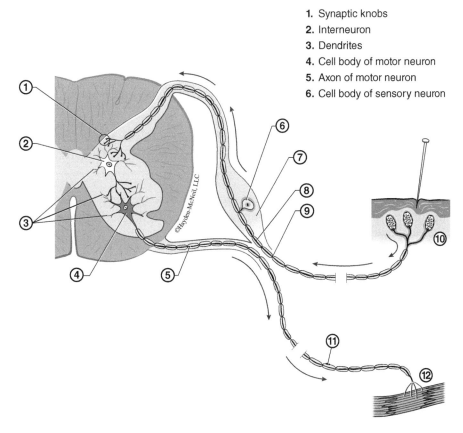

1. Synaptic knobs
2. Interneuron
3. Dendrites
4. Cell body of motor neuron
5. Axon of motor neuron
6. Cell body of sensory neuron
7. Dorsal root ganglion (spinal ganglion)
8. Axon of sensory neuron
9. Node of Ranvier
10. Sensory receptor (in skin)
11. Nucleus of Schwann cell (neuroglial cell)
12. Neuromuscular junction/ effector

Figure 2.24. Three Neuron Reflex Arc

Visceral Reflex Arc

In the viscera, the effectors are smooth muscle, cardiac muscle, or glands, and the reflex arc is controlled by the autonomic nervous system. This changes the pathway for the reflex arc.

In the autonomic nervous system there is still an afferent neuron and there are two neurons in the efferent pathway: a **preganglionic neuron** and a **postganglionic neuron**. These two neurons synapse outside the central nervous system in an autonomic ganglion. The location of the ganglion depends on which branch of the autonomic nervous system is involved in the reflex.

In the sympathetic nervous system the ganglia are located in a chain of ganglia very near the spinal cord. There is a chain on each side of the spinal cord. These ganglia (singular: ganglion) are called the **vertebral autonomic** or **paravertebral** or **sympathetic chain ganglia**. The sympathetic preganglionic efferent neuron leaves the central nervous system and synapses with the postganglionic neuron in one of the ganglia near the spinal cord. The postganglionic neuron leaves the ganglion and carries the impulse to the effector.

In the abdominal region there is a special circumstance with the sympathetic efferent neurons. In this region the preganglionic neuron passes through the vertebral autonomic ganglia without synapsing and actually synapses in a ganglion closer to the viscera. This second ganglion is a **collateral ganglion**. The postganglionic neuron would then leave the collateral ganglion and continue on to the viscera. There are three collateral ganglia on each side of the spinal cord: the celiac ganglia, the superior mesenteric ganglia, and the inferior mesenteric ganglia.

The **celiac** ganglia (SEE-lee-ak) are located on the each side of the celiac artery near the adrenal gland. The postganglionic neurons leaving these ganglia innervate the stomach, liver, pancreas, gallbladder, small intestine, spleen, and kidneys.

The **superior mesenteric** (MEZ-in-TER-ik) ganglia are located near the point where the superior mesenteric artery branches off the abdominal aorta. The postganglionic neurons that innervate the small and large intestines leave these ganglia.

The **inferior mesenteric** ganglia are the most inferior of the collateral ganglia. They are located near the point where the inferior mesenteric artery branches off the abdominal aorta. The postganglionic neurons that innervate the lower colon and rectum, urinary bladder, and reproductive organs leave these ganglia.

In the case of the parasympathetic nervous system the preganglionic neuron is much longer than in the sympathetic nervous system. The ganglia of the parasympathetic nervous system lie close to or in the wall of the viscera. The postganglionic neuron is short; since the ganglia are in or near the viscera, the postganglionic neuron only has a short distance to travel to the effector.

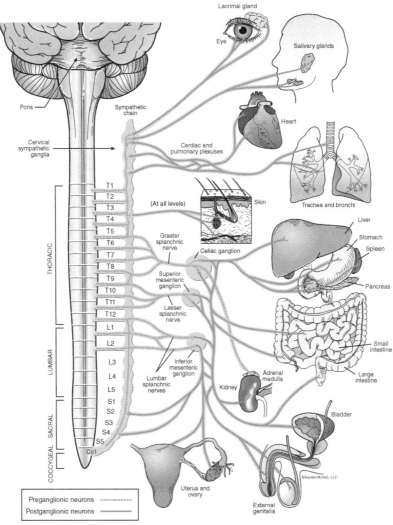

Anatomical Distribution of Sympathetic Output (thoracolumbar)

Figure 2.25. Sympathetic Nervous System

SPECIAL SENSES

We use our senses to observe and monitor our environment. Some of our senses, like pressure and temperature, are found in many areas of the body and are referred to as general senses. Other senses are localized in the head and are referred to as special senses. The more complex special senses in structure are the senses found in the ear—hearing and equilibrium. The most complex in function is the sense found in the eye—vision. We will first look at the structures of the ear followed by the structures of the eye.

SECTION A – THE EAR

The ear is divided into three sections: the external, middle, and inner ear. The external ear consists of the area exterior to the eardrum or tympanic membrane. The middle ear is the section that contains the ossicles (bones) and the auditory (Eustachian) tube. The inner ear contains the structures that contain the sensory receptors—the cochlea, vestibule, and semicircular canals.

The part of the external ear that is visible on the outside of the body is the **pinna** (PIN-a) or **auricle** (AW-ri-kl) of the ear. The canal that leads from the pinna into the temporal bone is the **external auditory** or **acoustic canal**. The **tympanic membrane** (tym-PAN-ik) or eardrum is at the end of this canal and serves as the border between the external ear and middle ear.

The middle ear is located between the tympanic membrane and the oval and round window. In the middle ear are the ossicles—**malleus** (MAL-ee-us), **incus** (ING-kus), and **stapes** (STAY-pez). The malleus is the ossicle attached to the tympanic membrane. It articulates with the incus or middle ossicle. This ossicle then articulates with the stapes, the innermost ossicle. The stapes sits in the oval window, an opening into the inner ear. Also found in the middle ear is the **auditory** or **Eustachian tube** (u-STAY-shun). This is a cartilaginous tube that connects the middle ear to the nasopharynx. It functions to equalize the pressure in the middle ear with the external air pressure. Normally the tube is closed except during yawning or swallowing. Unfortunately, the auditory tube can also be used by bacteria as a conduit into the middle ear and result in a middle ear infection.

The inner ear contains the **labyrinth** (**osseous** and **membranous**). The labyrinths are systems of tubular structures that make up the cochlea, vestibule, and semicircular canals. The osseous or bony labyrinth is the part of the tubular structures that are made up of bony walls. It forms the exterior of the inner ear. The membranous labyrinth consists of the ducts that are found inside the osseous labyrinth. The bony labyrinth can be subdivided into the cochlea, vestibule, and semicircular canals.

The **cochlea** (KOK-lee-ah) is a structure that resembles a snail shell. The outside of the cochlea is made up of the bony labyrinth and inside the membranous labyrinth is the **cochlear duct**. When the cochlea is observed on cross-section the cochlear duct has a triangular or wedge-like shape. The fluid-filled space superior to the cochlear duct is the **scala vestibuli** (SKAY-la ves-TIBU-lee) and the space inferior to the cochlear duct is the **scala tympani** (TIM-pa-nee). The **oval window** opens into the scala vestibuli. The scala tympani ends at the **round window**. On the floor of the cochlear duct is the **organ of Corti** or the **spiral organ** of the ear. This is the structure that contains the sensory receptors and nerve fibers for hearing. There are approximately 24,000 hair cells (neurons) in each cochlea. The nerve fibers of the cochlea leave as the **cochlear nerve** which merges with the vestibular nerve and leaves the ear as the eighth cranial nerve or the **vestibulocochlear nerve**.

The **vestibule** (VES-ti-bool) is involved in the sense of static equilibrium. It is found in the area between the cochlea and the semicircular canals. The oval window is on the side of the vestibule. The nerve fibers that carry the sense of equilibrium leave this area of the inner ear as the **vestibular nerve**, which will merge with the cochlear nerve as noted previously.

There are three **semicircular canals** situated at right angles to each other. This area of the inner ear is involved in the sense of dynamic equilibrium.

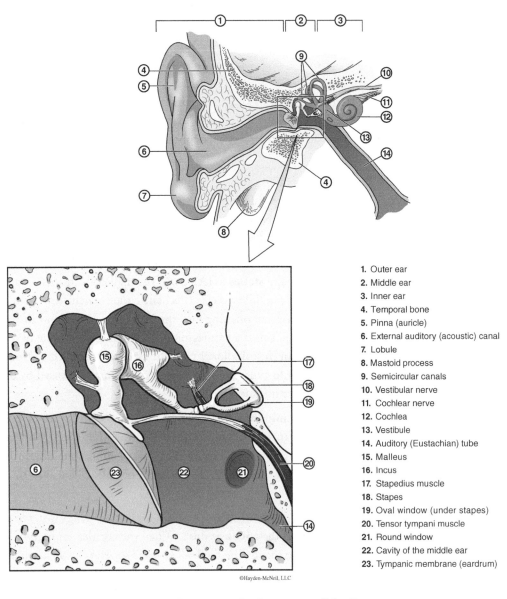

1. Outer ear
2. Middle ear
3. Inner ear
4. Temporal bone
5. Pinna (auricle)
6. External auditory (acoustic) canal
7. Lobule
8. Mastoid process
9. Semicircular canals
10. Vestibular nerve
11. Cochlear nerve
12. Cochlea
13. Vestibule
14. Auditory (Eustachian) tube
15. Malleus
16. Incus
17. Stapedius muscle
18. Stapes
19. Oval window (under stapes)
20. Tensor tympani muscle
21. Round window
22. Cavity of the middle ear
23. Tympanic membrane (eardrum)

©Hayden-McNeil, LLC

Figure 2.26. Structures of the Ear

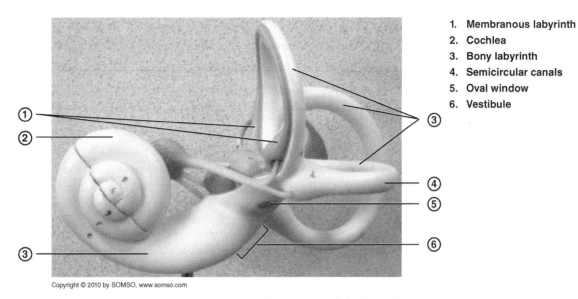

1. Membranous labyrinth
2. Cochlea
3. Bony labyrinth
4. Semicircular canals
5. Oval window
6. Vestibule

Copyright © 2010 by SOMSO, www.somso.com

Figure 2.27. Structures of the Inner Ear

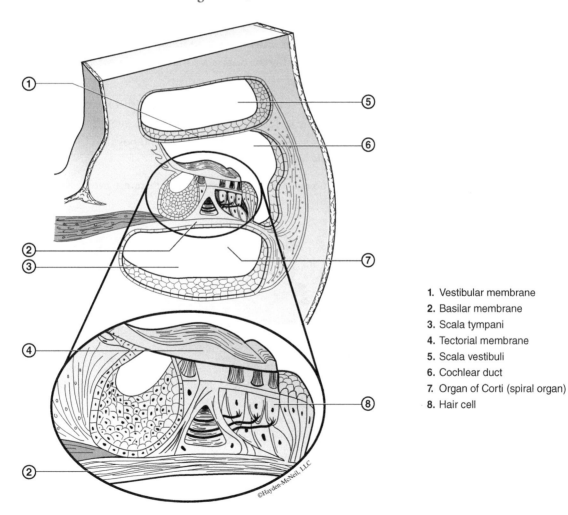

1. Vestibular membrane
2. Basilar membrane
3. Scala tympani
4. Tectorial membrane
5. Scala vestibuli
6. Cochlear duct
7. Organ of Corti (spiral organ)
8. Hair cell

©Hayden-McNeil, LLC

Figure 2.28. Cross Section of Cochlea

Otoscope

An otoscope is an instrument that is used to examine the outer ear canal and tympanic membrane. It consists of a light source, a speculum, and a magnifier to allow the observation of the outer ear.

Before you begin make sure the instrument is working. Turn it on and make sure there is a bright light emitting from the instrument. You will need to attach the largest speculum that can be comfortably inserted into the ear canal.

There are two common ways to hold the otoscope. The first way is to hold the otoscope like a hammer by gripping the top of the handle close to the light source. The otoscope can also be held like a pencil, between the thumb and the forefinger, with the ulnar aspect of the hand resting firmly but gently against the patient's cheek. This is a better way to hold the otoscope because if the individual turns or moves, the otoscope will move in unison with the individual's head. This will avoid possible injury to the ear canal or even the tympanic membrane.

Hold the otoscope in one hand as you insert the speculum into the ear canal and use your free hand to pull the outer ear gently up and back. This straightens the ear canal and improves visualization. As you are inserting the speculum you will be observing the ear canal. The sides of the ear canal are sensitive so be careful not to put too much pressure on the walls of the ear canal.

Do not advance the otoscope without observing the ear canal. You must see the path through the ear canal. It is not necessary to insert the speculum very far into the ear—the light extends well beyond the viewing tip.

The tip of the speculum should be angled slightly toward the person's nose to follow the normal angle of the canal. While looking through the otoscope, move it gently at different angles so that you can see the canal walls and eardrum. Stop at any sign of increased pain.

The ear canal will normally be skin colored, contain some small hairs, and some yellowish-brown or reddish-brown earwax. The tympanic membrane is normally pearly white or light gray color and transparent. You can normally see the ossicles pushing on the tympanic membrane. You can see a cone of light at the 5:00 position in the right ear and at the 7:00 position in the left ear. This is known as the light reflex.

You will now observe the other ear using the same procedure. After completing your examination please remove the speculum and disinfect it with alcohol.

Figure 2.29. Use of Otoscope

SECTION B – THE EYE

The eye is the organ of vision. It is small in size but complex in function. The eye is about an inch wide, an inch deep and an inch high. There are three layers to the eye: the sclera, the choroid, and the retina.

The outer layer is the **sclera** (SKLER-ah). The sclera is the white fibrous layer of the eyeball. When you look at the whites of someone's eyes you are looking at the sclera. The most anterior portion of the sclera is the transparent **cornea** (KOR-nee-ah). Contact lenses are placed on top of the cornea. This structure along with the lens helps focus an image on the retina. The cornea and the inside of the eyelids are covered by a protective mucous membrane called the **conjunctiva** (con-junk-TIE-vah). This is the membrane that is infected in pink eye or conjunctivitis.

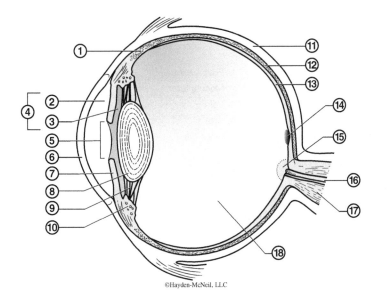

1. Ciliary body
2. Anterior chamber
3. Posterior chamber
4. Anterior cavity (contains aqueous humor)
5. Pupil
6. Cornea
7. Iris
8. Lens
9. Suspensory ligaments
10. Ciliary process
11. Sclera
12. Choroid
13. Retina
14. Fovea centralis (center of visual field)
15. Optic disk (blind spot)
16. Retinal blood vessels
17. Optic nerve
18. Posterior cavity (contains vitreous humor)

©Hayden-McNeil, LLC

Figure 2.30. Sagittal Section of Eye

The middle layer is the **choroid** (KO-royd). This is the layer that contains the blood vessels and pigment in the eye. The pigment in the choroid layer helps absorb light and prevent the scattering of the light. The anterior portion of the choroid is the **iris**. This is the pigmented portion of the eye that you see. In the center of the iris is an opening, the **pupil**. The iris is a muscle that controls the size of the pupil to control the amount of light entering the eye. The **lens** is behind the iris. The lens is a clear, flexible structure that is capable of changing shape. Surrounding the lens and controlling its shape is the **ciliary body** (SIL-ee-ar-ee). The lens is attached to folds of the ciliary body called **ciliary processes** by the **suspensory ligaments**. Contractions and relaxation of the ciliary body allows the eye to adjust for close and far vision.

The region of the eye anterior to the lens is the **anterior cavity**. This cavity can be further subdivided into the **anterior chamber** from the iris to the cornea and the **posterior chamber** from the iris to the lens. The anterior cavity contains a watery liquid called the **aqueous humor**. This fluid is produced by the ciliary body and circulated through the pupil and is absorbed in the canals of Schlemm in the anterior cavity. The aqueous humor provides nourishment for the lens and cornea. The area posterior to the lens is the **posterior cavity**. This area of the eye contains a gel-like fluid called the **vitreous humor**. This gel helps the eye keep its shape.

The inner layer of the eye is the **retina**. This is the nervous tissue of the eye. It contains the photoreceptors known as the rods and cones. Each retina has 5–6 million cones and 120 million rods. At the back of the eye there is the **optic disk** or **blind spot**. This is the point where the **optic nerve** leaves the eye. It does not contain any rods or cones so no image can be formed here. However, you do not normally recognize the fact that you have a blind spot in each eye because the field of vision from one eye compensates for the blind spot in the other eye.

There is a small area on the retina that can be recognized by a yellowish ring. This is the **macula lutea** (MAK-u-lah LOO-tee-a). It contains a high concentration of cones. This is the area that is important for your central vision. In the center of the macula is the **fovea centralis** (Fo-vee-ah). The fovea is the most sensitive area of the eye and is the area of the sharpest vision. The macula lutea is the portion of the retina destroyed in age-related macular degeneration. This destruction results in the loss of the center of vision but the peripheral vision is retained.

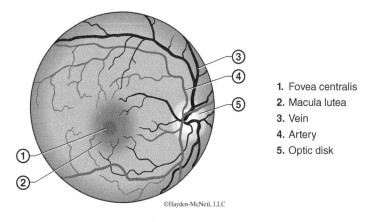

1. Fovea centralis
2. Macula lutea
3. Vein
4. Artery
5. Optic disk

©Hayden-McNeil, LLC

Figure 2.31. View of Retina through Pupil of Eye

External to the eyeball is the lacrimal apparatus. The **lacrimal glands** (LAK-ri-mahl) are found under the eyebrow at the outside edge of the eye. They produce the tears that cleanse and protect the eye. Tears contain lysozyme which has antibacterial activity. The tears wash across the surface of the eye and collect in the **lacrimal ducts** or **canals**. These ducts or canals empty into the **lacrimal sac** and eventually drain into the **nasolacrimal duct**. So tears eventually are drained into the nasal cavity. This is the reason the nose becomes congested when an individual cries.

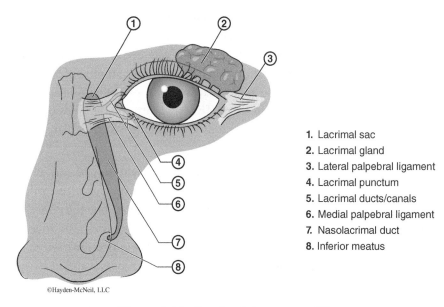

1. Lacrimal sac
2. Lacrimal gland
3. Lateral palpebral ligament
4. Lacrimal punctum
5. Lacrimal ducts/canals
6. Medial palpebral ligament
7. Nasolacrimal duct
8. Inferior meatus

©Hayden-McNeil, LLC

Figure 2.32. Lacrimal Apparatus of Eye

Ophthalmoscope

An ophthalmoscope is an instrument that is used to examine the interior of the eye. It consists of a series of lenses positioned in a rotating disk, a light source, and a series of mirrors to reflect the light source into the eye.

Before you begin make sure the instrument is working. Turn it on and make sure there is a bright light emitting from the instrument. The rotating disk of the ophthalmoscope should be on "0" to begin with.

Dim the lights in the room for the examination of a classmate. If the individual is wearing glasses request that he/she remove them. Ideally the classmate is seated comfortably. Instruct the individual to look at a fixed point in the room; it can be straight ahead or at a specific object somewhere in the room.

You will hold the instrument in your right hand to observe the classmate's right eye and in your left hand to observe the left eye. In addition, you will use your right eye to examine the classmate's right eye and your left eye for his or her left eye. Hold the ophthalmoscope so that your index finger is on the rotating disk.

Begin the examination at arm's length. You should see the red reflex. This is a reddish-orange reflection from the eye's retina. Move the ophthalmoscope closer to the eye until you are about 2 inches away. Do not let the instrument touch the eye. Look through the instrument and you should see a reddish, circular area—this is the interior of the eye. You will need to rotate the disk of the lenses to sharpen the focus. You should be able to observe the optic disk and blood vessels in the eye. The optic disk will be located towards the nasal side of the retina and will appear as a slightly oval, blood vessel free, slightly pinkish structure.

To observe the macula lutea, have your classmate look directly into the light of the ophthalmoscope. The macula lutea will be located on the temporal side of the optic disk, near the center of the retina. It should appear as a yellowish circle. You should not have your classmate looking directly at the light for more than 1–2 minutes.

Images of a normal retina as well as various pathological conditions will be available for viewing in the laboratory.

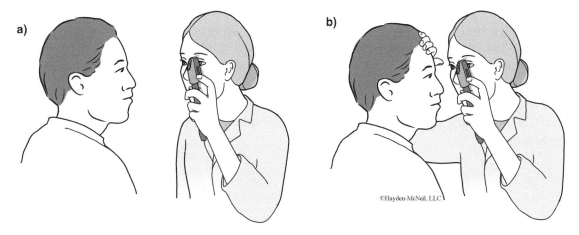

a) b)

©Hayden-McNeil, LLC

Figure 2.33. Procedure for Ophthalmoscope

Blind Spot

For this exercise you will use an illustration similar to the following available in the laboratory. This illustration will be used to detect the presence of the blind spot in each eye.

To test the right eye, close the left eye and stare at the plus sign on the illustration in the lab as it is moved from about 18 inches from the eye toward the face. At first, you will be able to see both the plus sign and the negative sign. Then as the image is moved closer to the face, at some point the negative sign will disappear. This will be the point at which it becomes focused on the optic disk of the retina.

Now you will perform this on the left eye. To test the left eye, close the right eye and stare at the negative sign and find the point at which the plus sign will disappear.

PART 5

THE ENDOCRINE SYSTEM

Communication within the body is achieved by both the nervous system and the endocrine system. The nervous system is responsible for rapid and precise responses. The endocrine system is responsible for sustained long-term control that is necessary for homeostasis.

The glands in the body are divided into exocrine and endocrine glands. Exocrine glands release the secretion into a duct, which will carry it to a specific location. For example, the salivary glands are exocrine glands and saliva is delivered by ducts to the oral cavity. Endocrine glands release the secretion into the bloodstream. It is carried through the blood by the body and will communicate with any cell that has a receptor for the particular chemical messenger. The endocrine system is a collection of glands that has the primary function of releasing hormones into the bloodstream. There are other organs and tissues in the body that produce and release hormones but are not included in the endocrine system. This is because the primary function of these other tissues, like the kidney, heart, and stomach, is not hormone production. The target tissues of the hormones are only the tissues that have a receptor for a specific hormone.

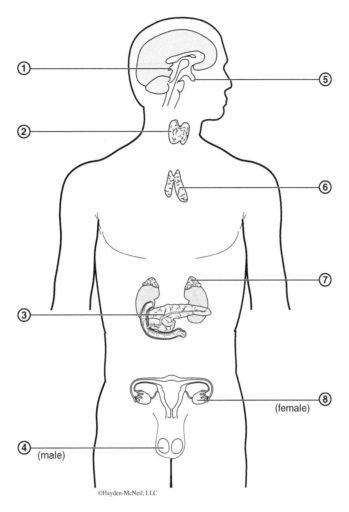

1. Pineal gland
2. Thyroid gland
3. Pancreas
4. Testes
5. Pituitary/hypophysis
6. Thymus
7. Adrenal gland
8. Ovary

©Hayden-McNeil, LLC

Figure 2.34. Endocrine Glands

Hypophysis/Pituitary

The **hypophysis** or **pituitary gland** is located inferior to the hypothalamus of the brain. It sits in the hypophyseal fossa of the sella turcica in the skull and is connected to the hypothalamus by way of the **infundibulum**. This is actually two different glands. The **anterior pituitary**, which is also known as the **adenohypophysis**, and the **posterior pituitary**, also called the **neurohypophysis**.

The anterior pituitary synthesizes seven different hormones, while the posterior pituitary does not synthesize any hormones. The posterior pituitary is the storage site for two hormones produced by the hypothalamus.

Pineal gland

The **pineal gland** or body is also located in the brain. It is a pinecone-shaped gland located posterior to the third ventricle and superior to the corpora quadrigemina of the midbrain. It is a combination of nervous tissue and endocrine tissue. The hormone secreted by the pineal gland is melatonin, which affects the diurnal rhythm and reproductive development.

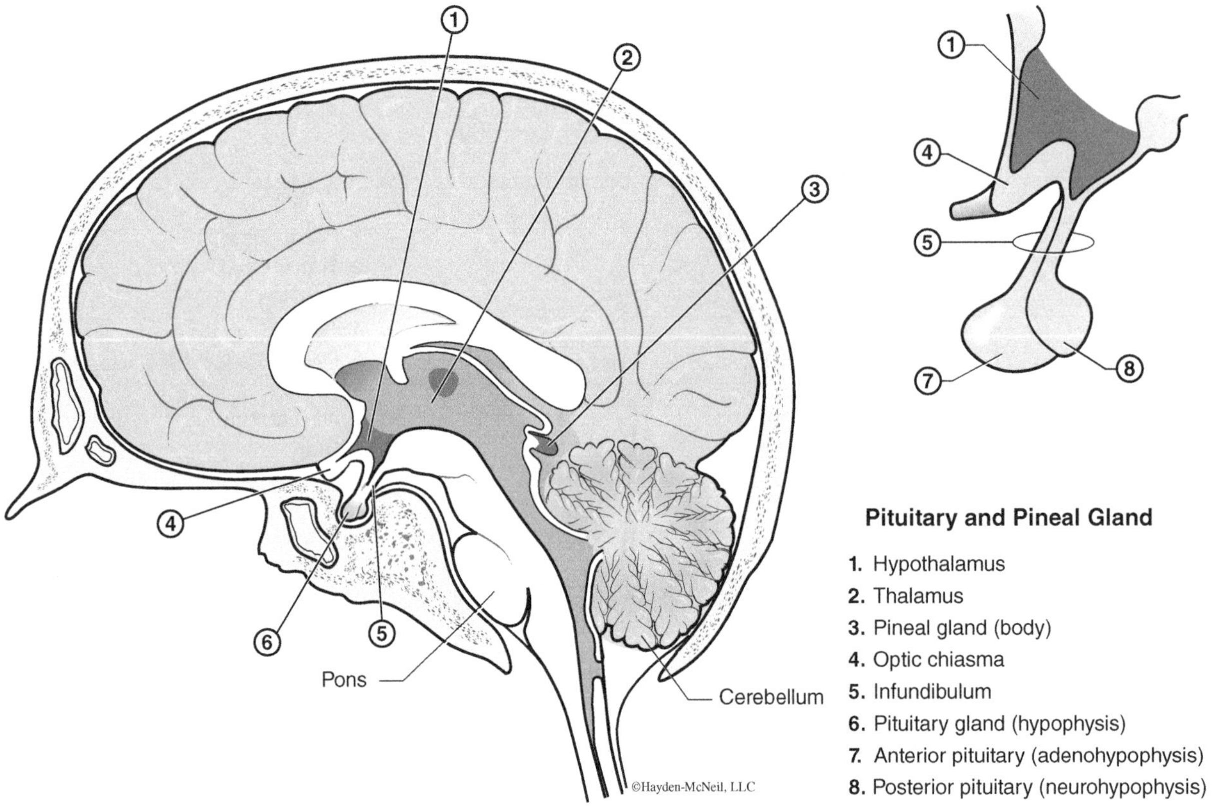
①
②
③
④
⑤
⑥
Pons
Cerebellum
①
④
⑤
⑦
⑧
Pituitary and Pineal Gland
1. Hypothalamus
2. Thalamus
3. Pineal gland (body)
4. Optic chiasma
5. Infundibulum
6. Pituitary gland (hypophysis)
7. Anterior pituitary (adenohypophysis)
8. Posterior pituitary (neurohypophysis)
©Hayden-McNeil, LLC

Figure 2.35. Pituitary and Pineal Gland

Table 2.1: Pituitary Hormones

HORMONE	TARGET	PRINCIPAL FUNCTION(S)
Anterior Pituitary/Adenohypophysis		
Growth Hormone (GH) Somatotropin (STH)	General body cells	Accelerates growth rate, especially muscle, bones
Thyroid-Stimulating Hormone (TSH)	Thyroid gland	Stimulates synthesis and secretion of thyroid hormones
Adrenocorticotropic Hormone (ACTH)	Adrenal Cortex (Zona Fasciculata)	Stimulates the synthesis and secretions of glucocorticoids and Cortisol
Follicle-Stimulating Hormone (FSH)	Ovary or Testis	Women: Stimulates development of ova in Graafian follicles and secretion of Estrogen Men: Promotes spermatogenesis in the seminiferous tubules
Luteinizing Hormone (LH in women); in men it is called Interstitial Cell Stimulating Hormone (ICSH)	Women: Ovary, especially the Corpus Luteum Men: Interstitial cells of testes	Women: Causes ovum to finish maturation then triggers ovulation; afterward, causes development of corpus luteum and production/secretion of Progesterone. Men: Stimulates production and secretion of testosterone.
Prolactin (Lactotrophic Hormone or LTH)	Mammary Glands	Stimulates (with progesterone) the maturation of the alveolar tissue and the production of milk.
Melanocyte Stimulating Hormone (MSH)	Melanocytes of skin	Increases melanin in skin to darken it, especially during pregnancy.
Posterior Pituitary/Neurohypophysis		
Antidiuretic Hormone (ADH)	Cells of the distal convoluted tubules of the kidneys	Stimulates reabsorption of water from urine back into the blood; causes dilution of blood plasma and increases blood pressure.
Oxytocin (OT)	Smooth muscle of the uterus; duct tissues of the mammary glands	Stimulates vigorous contractions of the uterus during labor; causes the release of milk from the alveoli of breasts ("letting down of milk").

Thyroid gland

The **thyroid gland** is located in the neck just below the larynx on either side of the trachea. It consists of two lobes on either side of the trachea and they are connected by a band of tissue that is called the isthmus. This gland secretes 3 hormones: tetraiodothyronine (thyroxine), triiodothyronine, and calcitonin. The thyroid is the target of TSH released by the anterior pituitary (adenohypophysis). Tetraiodothyronine (thyroxine), and triiodothyronine controls the metabolic rate. Calcitonin is involved in calcium homeostasis.

Parathyroid gland

The **parathyroid glands** are four very small nodules embedded into the back of the thyroid gland. They are not part of the thyroid gland. These glands are about the size and shape of a grain of rice, yet they are essential to life. The parathyroid hormone is the principal hormone in the homeostasis of calcium.

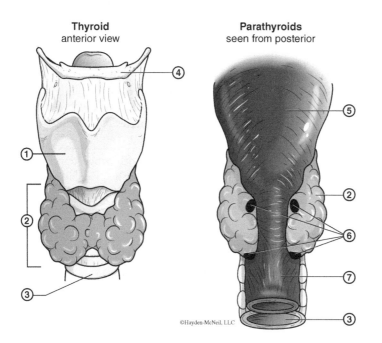

1. Thyroid cartilage of larynx
2. Thyroid gland
3. Trachea
4. Hyoid bone
5. Pharynx
6. Parathyroids
7. Esophagus

Figure 2.36. Thyroid and Parathyroid Glands

Thymus gland

The **thymus gland** is located in the upper thorax behind the sternum. It is at its largest and most active during childhood. Usually the thymus is at its maximum size by age two. After puberty the gland starts shrinking and is replaced by adipose tissue. The gland secretes thymosin, which is responsible for stimulating the growth and activity of T lymphocytes. As the gland shrinks, the amount of hormone production and T-cell production decreases. This results in a decrease in immune function with age.

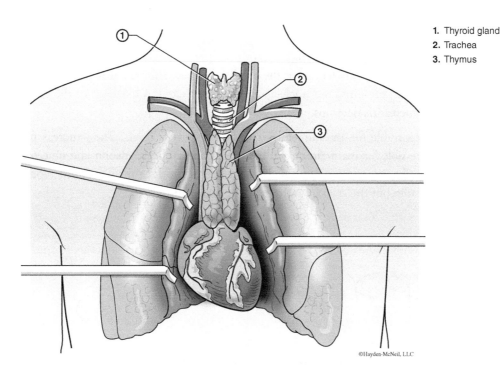

1. Thyroid gland
2. Trachea
3. Thymus

©Hayden-McNeil, LLC

Figure 2.37. Thymus Gland

Table 2.2: Thyroid, Parathyroid, and Thymus Hormones

HORMONE	TARGET	PRINCIPAL FUNCTION(S)
Thyroid Gland		
Thyroxine (T_4) and Triiodothyronine (T_3)	All body cells	Accelerates all metabolic processes and increases the use of oxygen (raises the metabolic rate). Stimulates growth and maturation of nervous system, bone, muscle.
Calcitonin (Thyrocalcitonin)	Cells of skeleton	Stimulates deposit of calcium salts in bone matrix by osteoblasts; lowers blood calcium ion concentration.
Parathyroid Gland		
Parathormone (PTH)	Skeleton, kidneys, and gastrointestinal tract	Increases blood calcium by stimulating osteoclasts to dissolve calcium salts from bone matrix into the bloodstream; by increasing reabsorption of calcium ions and excretion of phosphate ions into urine; enhances the uptake of calcium salts and phosphate from the gut.
Thymus Gland		
Thymosin	Structures of lymphatic system	Stimulates the development and maturation of the lymphatic system; B cells and T cells.

Pancreas

The **pancreas** is a long organ that extends across the abdomen from the spleen to the duodenum of the small intestine. This gland has both exocrine and endocrine functions. Its exocrine function is the production of digestive enzymes, which are delivered into the duodenum of the small intestine. The pancreas produces enzymes capable of digesting carbohydrates, lipids, proteins, and nucleic acids. When there is a blockage of the duct to carry these enzymes to the duodenum pancreatitis develops.

Its endocrine function is responsible for the homeostasis of blood glucose levels. The pancreas produces several hormones, but the two responsible for maintaining the blood glucose levels are insulin and glucagon. Individuals with type 1 diabetes mellitus have lost the ability of the pancreas to produce insulin. With type 2 diabetes the pancreas can still produce insulin but the cells are resistant to its stimulation.

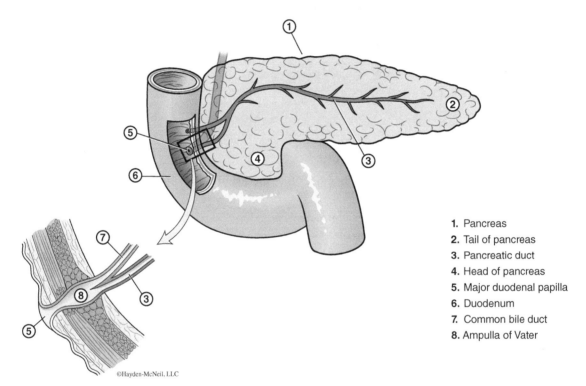

1. Pancreas
2. Tail of pancreas
3. Pancreatic duct
4. Head of pancreas
5. Major duodenal papilla
6. Duodenum
7. Common bile duct
8. Ampulla of Vater

©Hayden-McNeil, LLC

Figure 2.38. Pancreas

Adrenal Gland

The **adrenal** or **suprarenal glands** are on top of each kidney. This gland has an outer layer, the **cortex**, and the inner region, the **medulla**. Each region is unique in its functions. The cortex secretes glucocorticoids such as cortisol, mineralocorticoids such as aldosterone, and small amounts of gonadocorticoids. The adrenal cortex is stimulated by ACTH from the pituitary glands, particularly regarding the glucocorticoids. Aldosterone is responsible for regulating sodium levels in the body. Cortisol and its derivatives promote gluconeogenesis as well as functioning as anti-inflammatory agents. The gonadocorticoids are sex hormones, androgens and estrogens in small quantities.

The medulla is regulated by nerve impulses from the sympathetic nervous system. The adrenal medulla develops from neural tissue and secretes two hormones, epinephrine and norepinephrine. These two chemicals are also neurotransmitters in the sympathetic nervous system. Stimulation of the adrenal medulla by sympathetic fibers allows a sustained fight-or-flight response. Nervous system stimulation causes a rapid response, but it is not long-lasting, whereas hormones take longer to cause a response but last much longer.

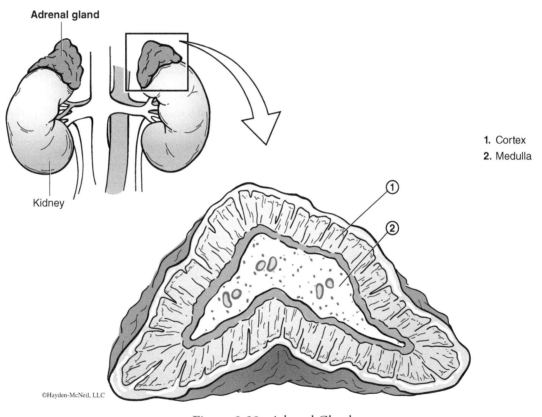

1. Cortex
2. Medulla

©Hayden-McNeil, LLC

Figure 2.39. Adrenal Gland

Table 2.3: Pancreatic and Adrenal Hormones

Hormone	Target	Principal Function(s)
Pancreas		
Insulin	Cells throughout the body, especially in the liver, fatty tissues, and muscles	Facilitates movement of glucose into cells across cell membranes; causes a drop in the blood sugar level; promotes glycogenesis and synthesis of proteins and fats; inhibits gluconeogenesis.
Glucagon	Liver	Opposes the action of insulin and helps prevent hypoglycemia; promotes glycogenolysis and gluconeogenesis; stimulates the breakdown of fats and use of fats as an energy source; causes a rise in blood sugar.
Adrenal Cortex		
Mineral corticoids (ex. Aldosterone)	Distal convoluted tubules of the kidney	Increases the reabsorption of sodium ions (and secondarily, chloride ions and water) from developing urine back into the blood.
Glucocorticoids (Cortisol and Corticosterone)	Cells throughout the body in general	Promotes gluconeogenesis in the liver; decreases protein synthesis; depresses the immune system; has a general anti-inflammatory effect.
Adrenal sex hormones (androgens and estrogen in tiny quantities)	Cells throughout the body	Usually minor effects in augmenting the promotions of secondary sex characteristics; adrenal tumors may cause over-secretion and development of sex-inappropriate characteristics; causes slight masculinization after menopause.
Adrenal Medulla		
Epinephrine and Norepinephrine	Circulatory, Respiratory, and Digestive systems; body cells in general	Increase blood pressure; increase vigor and rate of heart beat; increase blood flow to skeletal muscle and brain; increase airway diameter; decrease digestive function; general stimulation of metabolism; enhance the "fight-or-flight" response.

The Ovaries

The **ovaries** are paired organs found laterally to the uterus in the pelvic cavity in the female. They are about the size of an almond. The ovaries are responsible for producing the female sex cell, the ovum or egg. They also produce the female sex hormones, estrogens and progesterone. Estrogens are responsible for the development of secondary female sex characteristics such as breast development. Also, along with progesterone, estrogens control the menstrual cycle. In addition to the participation in the control of the menstrual cycle, progesterone is responsible for maintaining the uterine lining and inhibiting uterine contractions during pregnancy. Both hormones are under the control of the gonadotropins, FSH and LH, secreted by the anterior pituitary.

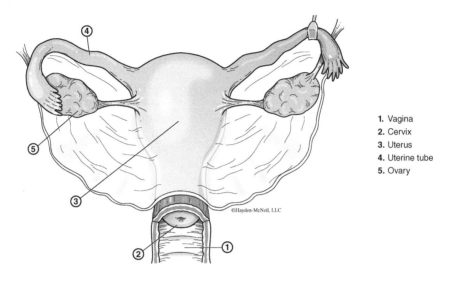

1. Vagina
2. Cervix
3. Uterus
4. Uterine tube
5. Ovary

©Hayden-McNeil, LLC

Figure 2.40. Ovary

The Testes

The **testes** (singular: testis) are paired organs found in the scrotum of the male. The testes are responsible for producing the male sex cell, sperm. In addition, testosterone is produced by the testes. Testosterone is responsible for development of the male secondary sex characteristics and the sexual drive.

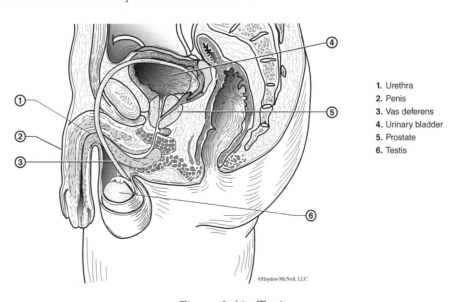

1. Urethra
2. Penis
3. Vas deferens
4. Urinary bladder
5. Prostate
6. Testis

©Hayden-McNeil, LLC

Figure 2.41. Testis

103

Table 2.4: Ovarian and Testicular Hormones

HORMONE	TARGET	PRINCIPAL FUNCTION(S)
Ovaries		
Estrogens (beta-estradiol, for example)	Female reproductive system, mammary glands, selected body tissues	Development and maintenance of female reproductive system; growth of the endometrium in the uterus; promotion of female secondary sex characteristics; feedback relationship with pituitary regarding production of LH, FSH; promotes closure of metaphyses.
Progesterone	Endometrium and mammary glands	Promotes the maturation of the endometrium to prepare it for implantation of embryo; continues to stabilize the endometrium throughout pregnancy; causes development and maturation of alveolar tissue within breasts; inhibits milk production by the mature alveolar tissue throughout pregnancy (sometimes unsuccessfully).
Testes		
Testosterone	Skeleton, muscle tissue, selected body tissues, male reproductive system	Promotes the development of male reproductive organs; promotes development of male secondary sex characteristics; promotes closure of metaphyses.

UNIT 3

BLOOD, CARDIOVASCULAR SYSTEM, LYMPHATICS, RESPIRATORY SYSTEM

This unit covers the cardiovascular system, which includes the heart, blood, and blood vessels, as well as the lymphatic system and the respiratory system. The lymphatics are important in maintaining fluid balance and returning extra fluid in the interstitial space to the blood.

The respiratory system is responsible for absorbing oxygen and excreting carbon dioxide. This provides the oxygen necessary for the proper function of the cardiovascular system as well as all the other tissues.

BLOOD

SECTION A – FORMED ELEMENTS

Blood is the medium that allows the cardiovascular system to perform its transport function. It is the only fluid tissue in the body. It transports oxygen and nutrients to the tissues and picks up waste products, including carbon dioxide, and returns to the proper organs for excretion. Blood is made up of plasma and the formed elements. The formed elements include the red blood cells, the white blood cells, and the platelets.

Red blood cells (RBCs) or **erythrocytes** (ah-RITH-ro-sites) are the most numerous of the formed elements. Mature erythrocytes do not contain a nucleus or other organelles. They are filled with hemoglobin. Since erythrocytes do not have a nucleus they are thinner in the center, referred to as biconcave disk. When you observe a blood smear, the red blood cells will appear pinkish with a pale center, due to the lack of a nucleus, and may appear to be in the background of the smear because they do not stand out on the slide. There is, however, a large quantity of them.

White blood cells (WBCs) or **leukocytes** (LOO-ko-sites) are not as numerous as red blood cells in the body or on a blood smear. There are 5 different types of white blood cells and they have a different appearance under the microscope. To view these cells they must be stained. The most common stain will make the white blood cells appear purple. The leukocytes will be stained purple and have a very obvious nucleus.

Platelets or **thrombocytes** (THROM-bo-sites) are not cells, they are fragments of cells. For this reason they are not very noticeable on the blood smear. They are stained purple like the leukocytes, but they appear as flecks on the slide. Their features are not distinguishable on the blood smear.

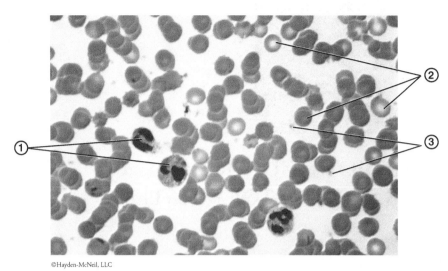

1. **Leukocytes – white blood cells**
2. **Erythrocytes – red blood cells**
3. **Platelets**

©Hayden-McNeil, LLC

Figure 3.1. Blood Smear

Table 3.1: Types of Formed Elements

FORMED ELEMENT	ALSO KNOWN AS	QUANTITY	FUNCTION
Erythrocytes	Red blood cells (RBCs)	5 million/mm³	Transport of oxygen and carbon dioxide
Leukocytes	White blood cells (WBCs)	5,000–10,000/ mm³	Protection against pathogens
Platelets	Thrombocytes	150,000–450,000/mm³	Involved in blood clotting

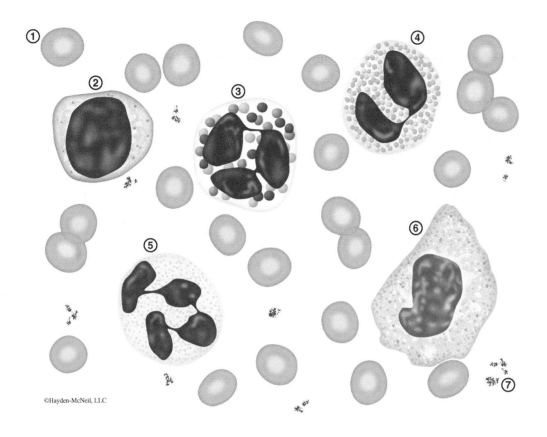

1. Red blood cell
2. Lymphocyte
3. Basophil
4. Eosinophil
5. Neutrophil
6. Monocyte
7. Platelets

©Hayden-McNeil, LLC

Figure 3.2. Blood Cells

Table 3.2: White Blood Cell Classifications

TYPE	FUNCTION	% OF WBCS
Neutrophils	Attacks and destroys bacteria	50–70%
Lymphocytes	Responsible for specific immunity, respond to bacterial and viral infections	20–40%
Monocytes	Becomes macrophages and engulfs large foreign particles	2–8%
Eosinophils	Responds during allergic reactions and parasitic infections	2–4%
Basophils	Promotes inflammation and healing of wounds	<1%

SECTION B – LABORATORY TESTS

In a clinical setting it is important to do various blood tests to evaluate patients. Some of the lab tests that are important to evaluate include: hematocrit, hemoglobin, and white blood cell differential.

The **hematocrit** (**HCT**) (he-MAT-o-krit) is a measurement of the proportion of blood that contains the red blood cells. To determine the hematocrit a microcapillary tube is filled with blood. This tube is then centrifuged to separate the plasma and the formed elements. A hematocrit reader can then determine the hematocrit value. This would be equal to the volume of the red blood cells divided by the total volume of blood and converted to a percentage. If the hematocrit is 38 this means that 38% of the blood's volume is composed of red cells.

A normal hematocrit is 42–52% for males and 37–47% for females. The hematocrit may be increased in erythrocytosis, polycythemia, COPD, or severe dehydration. The hematocrit may be decreased in anemia, cirrhosis, hemorrhage, vitamin deficiency, bone marrow failure, and renal disease.

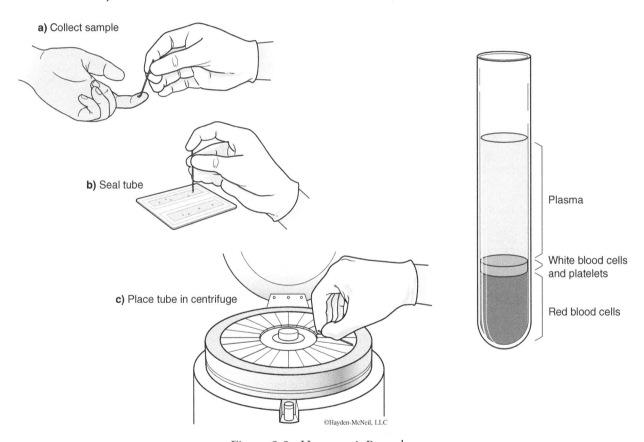

a) Collect sample

b) Seal tube

c) Place tube in centrifuge

©Hayden-McNeil, LLC

Plasma

White blood cells and platelets

Red blood cells

Figure 3.3. Hematocrit Procedure

Hemoglobin (**Hgb**) is the major component of red blood cells. It is responsible for the transport of oxygen, and when combined with oxygen gives the red blood cell its color. Measuring the hemoglobin is a good indication of the blood's ability to carry oxygen throughout the body. It is possible for an individual to have a normal red blood count and yet be anemic because the cells are not filled with hemoglobin. So to adequately evaluate an individual in addition to measuring the number of red blood cells, it is beneficial to measure the hemoglobin. There are several techniques for estimating or determining hemoglobin content such as the Tallquist method, the use of hemoglobinometer, or by colorimetry.

The hemoglobin is expressed as grams per 100 milliliter (mL) or 1 deciliter (dL) of blood. The normal hemoglobin is 14–18 g/dL for males and 12–16 g/dL for females. Hemoglobin may be increased with erythrocytosis, polycythemia, severe dehydration, and congenital heart disease. It may be decreased with anemia, hemoglobin abnormalities, hemorrhage, iron deficiency, and bone marrow failure.

A **red blood cell count** can be used to determine anemia as well as abnormalities in the red blood cells or conditions affecting the erythrocytes. A normal red blood cell count is recorded as the number of cells per microliter (mcL). The normal red blood cell count for males is 4.7 to 6.1 million cells per mcL, and 4.2 to 5.4 million cells per mcL for females.

An increased red blood cell count may indicate congenital heart disease, polycythemia, dehydration, or cor pulmonale (right sided heart failure due to lung disease). A decreased red blood cell count may indicate anemia, hemorrhage, bone marrow failure, kidney disease, malnutrition, or overhydration.

The red blood cells carry oxygen from the lungs to the rest of the body and carry carbon dioxide back to the lungs so it can be exhaled. If the number of erythrocytes is low the body may not be getting the oxygen it needs. The danger of an increase in red blood cells is that it causes the blood viscosity to increase; this makes it harder for the heart to pump the blood. The liver and spleen become congested as the increased viscosity causes a decrease in blood flow. Eventually, the thick, slow-moving blood can result in clotting and blood vessel obstruction.

The **white cell differential count** reports each type of leukocyte as a percentage of the total white blood cell count. This test is especially helpful in the evaluation of an individual with an infection, neoplasm, allergy, or immunosuppression. It can be used by the physician to determine if there is an abnormal amount of any particular white blood cell which can help with a diagnosis. For example, if the percentage of neutrophils is elevated it could indicate an acute infection somewhere in the body.

Table 3.3: White Blood Cell Count and Differential Count

TYPE OF WBC	PERCENT OF TOTAL	ACTUAL COUNT
Normal		5000 – 10,000/mm^3
Differential:		
Neutrophils	55 – 70%	2500 – 8000/mm^3
Lymphocytes	20 – 40%	1000 – 4000/mm^3
Monocytes	2 – 8%	100 – 700/mm^3
Eosinophils	1 – 4%	50 – 500/mm^3
Basophils	0.5 – 1.0%	25 – 100/mm^3

Table 3.4: Possible Intrepretation of Differential Count Results

Type of WBC	Increased Levels	Decreased Levels
Total WBC count	infection, leukemia, tissue necrosis, inflammation, dehydration	drug toxicity, bone marrow failure, overwhelming infections, dietary deficiencies, autoimmune disease
Neutrophils	acute suppurative infection, myelocytic leukemia, trauma, Cushing's disease, inflammatory disorders	aplastic anemia, dietary deficiency, overwhelming bacterial infection, viral infection, Addison's disease
Lymphocytes	chronic bacterial infection, viral infection, lymphocytic leukemia, multiple myeloma, infectious mononucleosis, infectious hepatitis	leukemia, sepsis, immunodeficiency diseases, lupus erythematosus, later stages of HIV
Monocytes	chronic inflammatory disorders, viral infections, tuberculosis, chronic ulcerative colitis, parasites	drug therapy, prednisone
Eosinophils	parasitic infections, allergic reactions, eczema, leukemia, autoimmune diseases	increased adrenosteroid production
Basophils	myeloproliferative disease, leukemia	acute allergic reactions, hyperthyroidism, stress reactions

Section C – Blood Types

On the surface of the cells of the body are markers or antigens that are determined genetically. These antigens are glycoproteins that identify the cell as belonging or not belonging to the body. Red blood cells have several different antigens on their surface, but the most important are the ABO group and the Rh group. An individual's blood type is determined by which antigens are found on the surface of his/her red blood cell. In addition to the antigens, which are also known as agglutinogens (AG-lutin-ahjins), the plasma usually contains antibodies or agglutinins (AHGLUE-tinins) which are proteins that react with any red blood cell carrying an antigen different than the body's own red blood cells. When the antigen and the antibody interact it causes the red blood cells to clump or agglutinate (ah-GLUE-tin-ate) and possibly hemolyze. As a result of this possible interaction, which would be detrimental to an individual, it is important to determine an individual's blood type prior to transfusion of any blood.

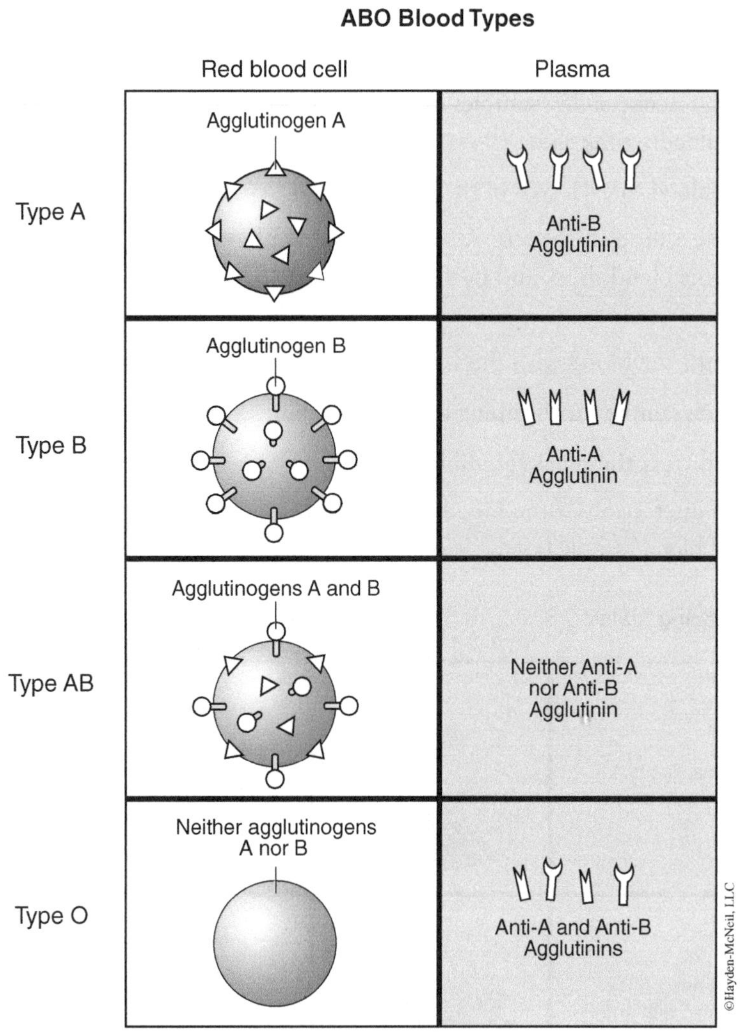

ABO Blood Types

For a transfusion to be successful, the recipient must lack antibodies (agglutinins) directed against the transfused cells. Type AB lacks antibodies against types A, B, and of course O, so it is sometimes called a **universal recipient**. Type O cells have no agglutinogens, and so cannot be agglutinated by type A, B, or AB, so this type is called a **universal donor**. However, blood must always be cross-matched before transfusing, except in dire emergency.

Agglutinogen = antigen
Agglutinin = antibody

Figure 3.4. Blood Types

Blood Typing Procedure

To perform blood typing on a sample of blood:

The supplies needed include microscope slides, samples of artificial blood, anti-A serum, anti-B serum, and anti-D (Rh) serum, toothpicks, and a blood typing slide.

1. Add a drop of the artificial blood to each well of the slide.

2. In the well labeled "A" place a drop of the anti-A serum with the blood drop, in the well labeled "B" place a drop of anti-B serum with the blood drop, and in the well labeled "Rh" place a drop of the anti-D serum with the blood drop.

3. Using separate toothpicks mix the blood with the antiserum.

4. Within 2 minutes check each sample for clumping or agglutination.

5. After determining the blood type, the slides should be cleaned.

6. Based on the results of the interaction of the blood with the antiserum, you should be able to determine the blood type of each artificial blood sample tested.

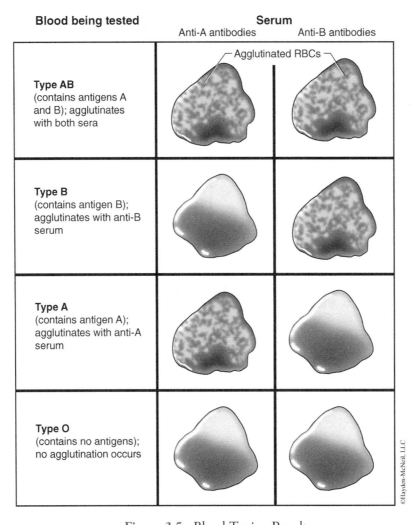

Figure 3.5. Blood Typing Results

PART 2

HEART

The heart is composed of cardiac muscle and is located between the two lungs in the mediastinum. The sternum is located anterior to the heart and the vertebral column is located posteriorly. This positioning allows for chest compressions. The heart can be compressed between the two bones. It is not a very big organ; it measures about 4-1/2 inches long and 3-1/2 inches wide.

The primary function of the heart is to circulate the blood through the body and the lungs. The normal heart rate is 60–100 beats/minute, 24 hours a day, every day. During a normal day the heart beats about 100,000 times and pumps about 2,000 gallons of blood.

SECTION A – EXTERNAL ANATOMY OF THE HEART

Let's begin by examining the exterior of the heart. The distal end of the heart points downward and to the left, this is the **apex** of the heart. The superior end of the heart where the great vessels enter and leave the heart is the **base**.

The heart is surrounded by a **fibrous pericardium** (PER-ah-KAR-de-um) which is lined with the **serous pericardium**. The fibrous pericardium consists of dense connective tissue. Its functions include providing protection for the heart, helping anchor the heart in the thorax, and preventing the heart from overexpanding when there is an increase in blood volume.

Lining the fibrous pericardium is the serous pericardium. This membrane has two layers, the **parietal pericardium** lining the fibrous pericardium and the **visceral pericardium** adhering to the surface of the heart. Between the two layers is the **pericardial cavity** which is lined with a very thin layer of serous fluid to prevent friction during the contraction of the heart.

The heart wall consists of three layers—the **epicardium**, the **myocardium**, and the **endocardium**. The outer layer is the epicardium which is also the visceral pericardium. This layer contains the blood vessels delivering oxygen to the myocardium as well as lymphatic vessels and nerve fibers. The middle layer is the myocardium. This layer is made up of the cardiac muscle, which is striated involuntary muscle responsible for the contraction of the heart. The inner layer is the endocardium, which lines the chambers of the heart, covers the heart valves, and is continuous with the inner lining of blood vessels. It contains the Purkinje fibers and blood vessels. Its function is to form a smooth, protective inner layer.

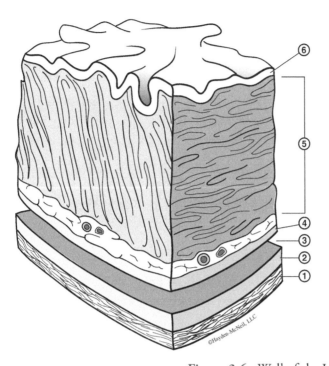

1. Fibrous pericardium
2. Parietal pericardium
3. Pericardial cavity
4. Visceral pericardium (epicardium)
5. Myocardium
6. Endocardium

Figure 3.6. Wall of the Heart

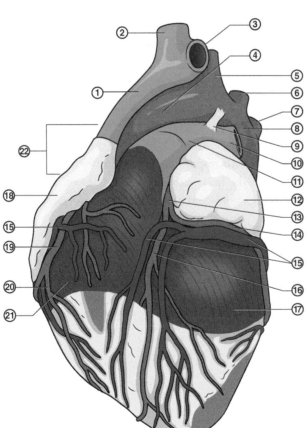

1. Superior vena cava
2. R. brachiocephalic v.
3. L. brachiocephalic v.
4. Ascending aorta
5. Brachiocephalic a.
6. L. common carotid a.
7. L. subclavian a.
8. Aortic arch
9. Ligamentum arteriosum
10. L. pulmonary a.
11. Pulmonary trunk
12. L. atrium w/ auricle
13. L. coronary a.
14. Circumflex a.
15. Cardiac veins
16. L. anterior descending a.
17. L. ventricle
18. R. atrium w/ auricle
19. R. coronary a.
20. Marginal a.
21. R. ventricle
22. Base of heart

Figure 3.7. Anterior View of the Heart

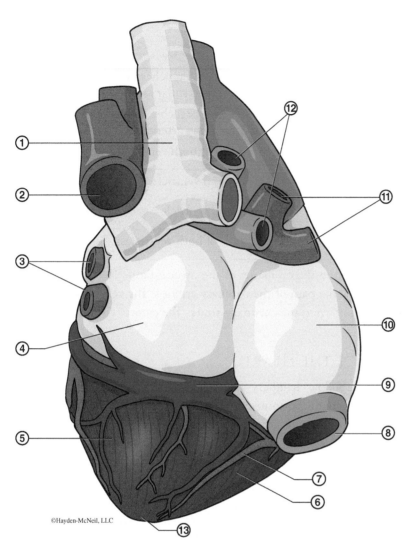

1. Trachea
2. Aorta
3. L. pulmonary v.
4. L. atrium
5. L. ventricle
6. R. ventricle
7. Posterior interventricular a.
8. Inferior vena cava
9. Coronary sinus
10. R. atrium
11. R. pulmonary v.
12. R. pulmonary arteries
13. Apex

©Hayden-McNeil, LLC

Figure 3.8. Posterior View of the Heart

Coronary Arteries

The cardiac muscle is in constant need of oxygen and nutrients to supply its energy supply and the coronary arteries are responsible. The **right** and **left coronary arteries** are the first arteries to branch off the aorta. The openings to the coronary arteries can be found just superior to the cusps of the aortic semilunar valve.

These two coronary arteries branch several times to ensure the entire cardiac muscle receives the necessary nutrients. The left coronary artery gives rise to the **left anterior descending artery** and the **circumflex artery**. The left anterior descending artery travels down the interventricular sulcus on the anterior surface of the heart to supply both ventricular walls. The circumflex artery travels around to the back of the heart in a groove between the left atrium and the left ventricle. It supplies the wall of the left atrium and ventricle. The arteries continue to branch into smaller arteries that penetrate the myocardium and eventually give rise to the capillaries.

The right coronary artery travels through a groove between the right atrium and ventricle. It gives rise to two arteries, the **posterior interventricular artery** and the **marginal artery**. The posterior interventricular artery travels the interventricular sulcus on the posterior surface of the heart and supplies the walls of both ventricles. The marginal artery follows the lower border of the right side of the heart and supplies both the right atrium and the right ventricle.

115

Table 3.5: Coronary Arteries

ARTERY	SOURCE	TISSUES SUPPLIED
Coronary artery, right	ascending aorta	right side of heart, branches into marginal and posterior interventricular arteries
Coronary artery, left	ascending aorta	left side of heart, branches into circumflex and anterior descending arteries
Posterior interventricular artery	right coronary artery	posterior walls of both ventricles
Marginal	right coronary artery	right atrium and ventricle
Circumflex	left coronary artery	left atrium and ventricle
Anterior descending artery	left coronary artery	anterior walls of both ventricles

The coronary arteries deliver the nutrient-rich blood to the capillaries of the myocardium. The blood then drains into the **cardiac veins**. These veins generally follow the path of the coronary arteries. The veins drain into a large vein located on the posterior surface of the heart known as the **coronary sinus**. The coronary sinus drains directly into the right atrium.

SECTION B – INTERNAL ANATOMY OF THE HEART

On the interior of the heart it is easy to see the four hollow chambers. The two on the top are the **right** and **left atria** (A-tre-ah) (singular, atrium (A-tre-um)) and the two on the bottom are the **right** and **left ventricles** (VENT-tri-klz). The atria collect the blood returning to the heart and the ventricles pump the blood out into the arteries.

The atria have thin walls and small earlike projections known as **auricles** (AW-rah-klz) that allow some additional expansion of the atria to hold additional blood returning to the heart. The right and left atria are separated by a wall called the **interatrial septum**. This prevents the blood from the two atria mixing. On the surface of the interatrial septum in the right atrium there is a depression called the **fossa ovalis**. This is the remnant of the foramen ovale, an opening present between the two atria in the fetus. In the right atrium and in both auricles there are ridges of myocardium on the inner surface which are known as the pectinate muscles.

The vessels entering the right atrium are the **superior vena cava**, the **inferior vena cava**, and the coronary sinus. These vessels are veins returning deoxygenated, or oxygen poor, blood from the body. The vessels entering the left atrium are the **pulmonary veins**, two from the right lung and two from the left lung. These veins are returning oxygenated, or oxygen rich, blood from the lungs.

In the heart there are valves called atrioventricular valves (AV valves) between the atria and ventricles. These valves provide for one-way flow of blood from each atrium into each ventricle by preventing backflow of blood into the atria when the ventricles contract.

On the right side of the heart is the **right atrioventricular** or **tricuspid valve**. This valve consists of three flaps or cusps that are responsible for the name. The valve opens when the pressure in the right atrium is greater than the pressure in the right ventricle. At that time the cusps lay against the ventricular wall out of the way.

Attached to the ventricular side of the cusp are strong, fibrous threads or strings called the **chordae tendineae** (KOR-day-TEN-dah-nay) or the heart strings. These strings arise from the **papillary muscles** (PAP-i-LER-ee) that are cardiac muscle tissue projecting from each ventricular wall. When the ventricle contracts the papillary muscles contract as well; this prevents the cusps from projecting into the right atrium as the result of the increased pressure in the right ventricle.

The wall of the right ventricle is thinner than the wall of the left ventricle. The right ventricle pumps blood out to the lungs for oxygenation. The lungs are relatively close to the heart and are a low pressure system so it is not necessary for this ventricle to generate a high pressure. The **interventricular septum** forms the wall between the two ventricles.

In addition to the valve between the atria the ventricles also have a valve at the opening of the artery that exits each ventricle. These are the **semilunar valves**. The artery leaving the right ventricle is the **pulmonary trunk** and the valve is the **pulmonary** or **pulmonic semilunar valve**. When the right ventricle contracts the tricuspid valve closes as the pressure in the ventricle increases. Initially the pulmonary semilunar valve is closed. As the pressure increases in the right ventricle the ventricular pressure exceeds the arterial pressure in the pulmonary trunk and the pulmonary semilunar valve is pushed open. Blood flows out of the ventricle and into the pulmonary trunk which divides into the **right** and **left pulmonary arteries**. The ventricle then relaxes and the pressure pushing the blood decreases. The blood in the pulmonary trunk begins to flow back toward the ventricle and the blood collects in the cusps of the semilunar valve closing it. This prevents the backflow of arterial blood into the ventricle. There is a fibrous band of tissue that extends from the top of the pulmonary trunk to the aortic arch. This is the **ligamentum arteriosum**, which is the remnant of the ductus arteriosus, an opening between these two structures in the fetal circulation.

On the left side of the heart the vessels returning blood to the atrium are the four pulmonary veins. The atrioventricular valve on the left side is the **bicuspid** or **mitral valve**. This valve has two flaps or cusps (bicuspid) and has been described as resembling a miter (mitral). This valve works like the tricuspid valve and prevents backflow of the blood from the left ventricle into the left atrium. It has chordae tendineae and papillary muscles attached just like on the right side of the heart.

The wall of the left ventricle is much thicker than the wall of the right ventricle. It pumps oxygenated, or oxygen rich, blood out to the tissues of the body. It has to push the blood to all parts of the body against greater resistance. The thickness of the left ventricular wall helps to identify which chamber is being observed.

The artery leaving the left ventricle is the **aorta** and the semilunar valve at its base is the **aortic** or **aortic semilunar valve**. This semilunar valve works the same as the pulmonary semilunar valve. When the left ventricle contracts the bicuspid valve closes and, initially, the aortic semilunar valve is closed. As the pressure increases in the left ventricle the pressure exceeds the pressure in the aorta and the aortic semilunar valve is pushed open. Blood flows out of the ventricle and into the aorta. The ventricle then relaxes and the pressure pushing the blood decreases. The blood begins to flow back toward the ventricle and the blood collects in the cusps of the semilunar valve closing it. This prevents the backflow of the blood into the ventricle.

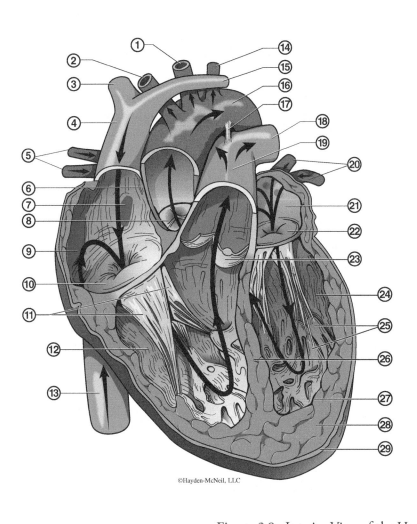

©Hayden-McNeil, LLC

1. L. common carotid a.
2. Brachiocephalic a.
3. R. brachiocephalic v.
4. Superior vena cava
5. R. pulmonary veins
6. Interatrial septum
7. Fossa ovalis
8. Aortic semilunar valve
9. R. atrium
10. Tricuspid valve
11. Chordae tendineae
12. R. ventricle
13. Inferior vena cava
14. L. subclavian a.
15. L. brachiocephalic v.
16. Aorta
17. Ligamentum arteriosum
18. L. pulmonary a.
19. Pulmonary trunk
20. L. pulmonary v.
21. L. atrium
22. Bicuspid valve (mitral)
23. Pulmonary semilunar valve
24. L. ventricle
25. Papillary muscles
26. Interventricular septum
27. Endocardium (lines each chamber)
28. Myocardium
29. Epicardium (covers the surface)

Figure 3.9. Interior View of the Heart

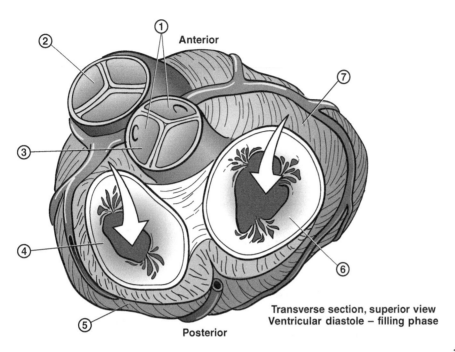

Transverse section, superior view
Ventricular diastole – filling phase

1. Opening to coronary arteries
2. Pulmonary semilunar valve
3. Aortic semilunar valve
4. L. AV (bicuspid) valve (mitral valve)
5. L. ventricle
6. R. AV (tricuspid) valve
7. R. ventricle

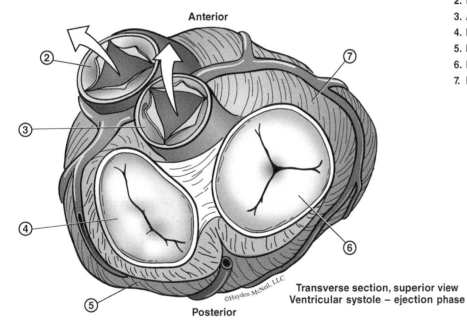

Transverse section, superior view
Ventricular systole – ejection phase

Figure 3.10. Superior View of the Heart Valves

SECTION C – DISSECTION OF THE SHEEP HEART

The sheep's heart is similar to the human heart. Dissecting this specimen will allow you to examine structures in a preserved specimen that you have been studying on the models. The method you will use to dissect this heart will also help you study the blood flow through the heart.

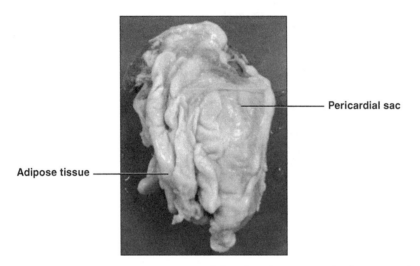

Pericardial sac

Adipose tissue

Figure 3.11. Anterior View of the Sheep's Heart with the Pericardium

You will need gloves, a dissection tray, a straight pin, a blunt-end probe, scissors, and scalpel. Carefully handle the equipment to prevent injury. All biological material must be disposed of properly.

The specimen will usually have extraneous material such as lung tissue or the trachea still attached and it will still have the fibrous pericardium covering the heart. The first chore will be to remove any extraneous material and the fibrous pericardium. The fibrous pericardium is attached at the base of the heart but is not attached to the apex of the heart. Take note of how strong this tissue is. The inner surface is smooth; this is the parietal pericardium. The space between this tissue and the heart is the pericardial cavity. The visceral pericardium is on the surface of the heart. You will note there is a fat layer on the heart; the amount of fat on each heart may vary.

Before the dissection begins you must find the front of the heart. This can be identified by the left anterior descending artery. Another way to distinguish the front from the back is the fact that the vessels entering the heart enter on the posterior surface. Once you have identified the front of the heart, you will place the straight pin along the left anterior descending artery so that you will make the incisions on the correct surface. Now make sure you can distinguish the right side of the heart from the left so you are entering the correct chambers.

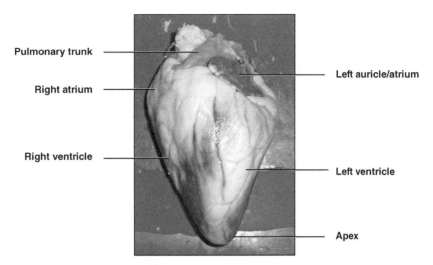

Figure 3.12. Anterior View of the Heart with the Pericardium Removed

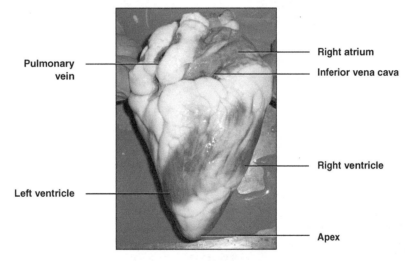

Figure 3.13. Posterior View of the Heart with the Pericardium Removed

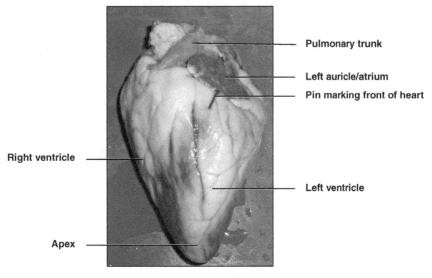

Figure 3.14. Anterior View of the Heart Marked with Straight Pin

You are now ready to begin. The easiest way to open the chambers is to use the blunt end probe as a guide. Using the handle end of the probe you will want to find the superior vena cava entering the right atrium. Manipulate the probe through the right atrium and exit through the inferior vena cava. Leave the probe in place. You now have the probe passing through the right atrium which will be the first chamber you open. The incision you will make is on the back of the heart. This will be the only incision on the back of the heart; all the rest will be on the front. Using the scalpel you will cut through the right atrial tissue until you can lift the probe straight out of the chamber. You may need to use the scissors to clip the corners of the auricle so that you can look down into the atrium.

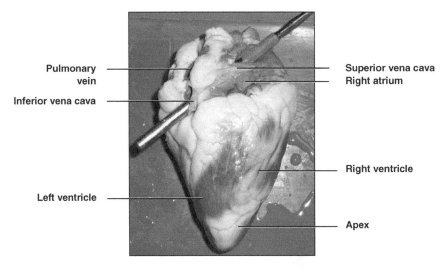

Figure 3.15. Posterior View of Heart with Probe Through Right Atrium

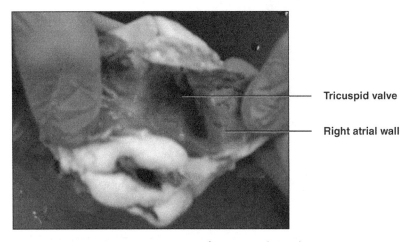

Figure 3.16. Superior View of Heart with Right Atrium Open

Now pass the handle of the probe through the tricuspid valve into the right ventricle. Advance it to the bottom of this ventricle. You will note that the right ventricle does not extend to the apex of the heart. This next incision will be on the front of the heart. You will cut through the myocardium until you free the probe again. This will be a much deeper cut since the wall of the ventricle is much thicker than the wall of the atrium. After releasing the probe open the right ventricle and observe. Locate the cusps of the tricuspid valve, the chordae tendineae, and the papillary muscles. Note the thickness of the ventricular wall.

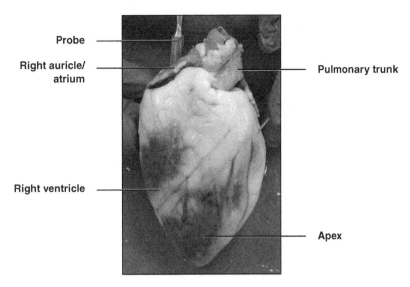

Figure 3.17. Anterior View of Heart with Probe Inserted into Right Ventricle

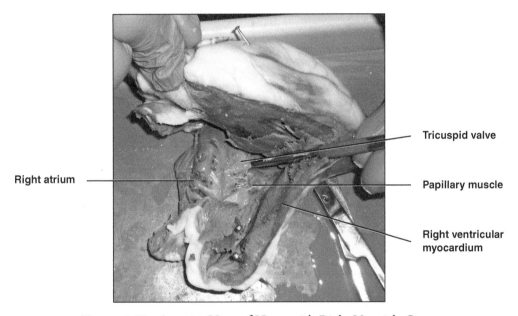

Figure 3.18. Anterior View of Heart with Right Ventricle Open

Blood leaves the right ventricle through the pulmonary trunk so this will be the next structure you will cut. You will use the handle of the probe to enter the trunk. You will find the opening to this artery on the medial surface of the ventricle near the interventricular septum, placing the probe inferior to the tricuspid valve. Once the probe is placed, cut on the anterior surface to release the probe. Open the artery and observe the smooth surface in this blood vessel. Use the bent end of the probe to locate the cusps of the pulmonary semilunar valve. You can usually find two of the three cusps; usually the third cusp has been cut during the incision.

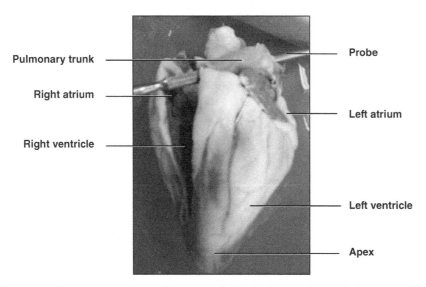

Pulmonary trunk

Right atrium

Right ventricle

Probe

Left atrium

Left ventricle

Apex

Figure 3.19. Anterior View of Heart with Probe Inserted into Pulmonary Trunk

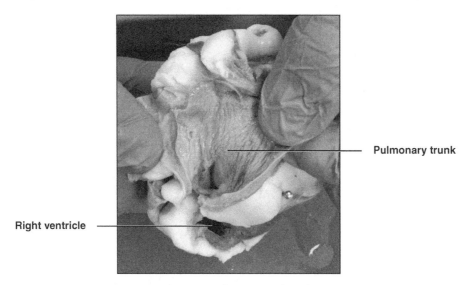

Pulmonary trunk

Right ventricle

Figure 3.20. Superior View of Heart with Pulmonary Trunk Open

You have successfully opened the right side of the heart and at the same time followed the blood flow through that side.

Superior & Inferior Vena Cava → Right Atrium → Right Ventricle → Pulmonary Trunk

You are now ready to move on to the left side of the heart. Turn the heart over and on the posterior surface of the left atrium you need to locate one of the pulmonary veins entering the left atrium. Insert the handle of the probe into the left atrium, through the mitral valve into the left ventricle to the apex of the heart. This time you will open both the atrium and ventricle. Turn the heart over so that you can cut on the anterior surface. This will be a very deep incision. You are going to cut through the myocardium on the anterior surface to free the probe. You now have both the atrium and ventricle open. Once again locate the cusps, chordae tendineae, and papillary muscles. Compare the thickness of the left ventricular wall to the thickness of the right ventricle. There is a very obvious difference.

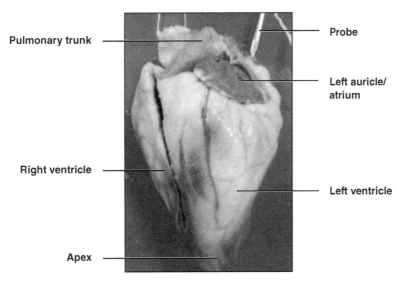

Figure 3.21. Anterior View of Heart with Probe Inserted into Left Chambers of Heart

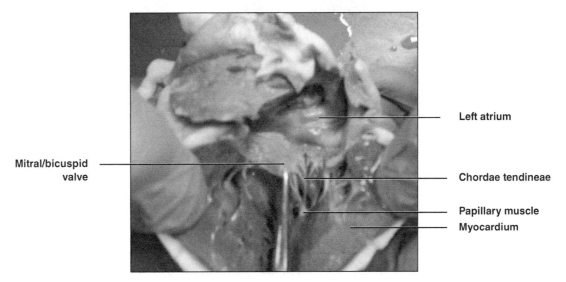

Figure 3.22. Anterior View of Heart with Left Ventricle

Now you will make the final incision into the aorta. You will insert the handle of the probe into the aorta. To do this you will find the opening to the aorta by inserting the probe underneath the mitral valve near the interventricular septum. Your incision will again be on the anterior surface of the heart. You will need to cut through the pulmonary trunk to open the aorta since the pulmonary trunk is anterior to the aorta. Once you have freed the probe, locate the cusps of the aorta semilunar valve.

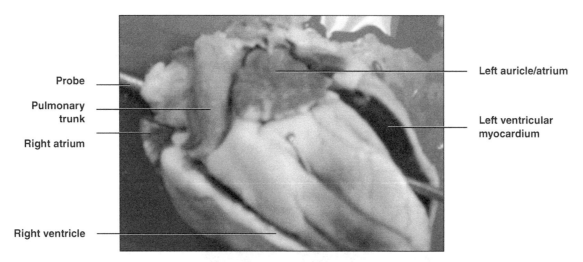

Probe
Pulmonary trunk
Right atrium

Left auricle/atrium
Left ventricular myocardium

Right ventricle

Figure 3.23. Anterior View of Heart with Probe Inserted into Aorta

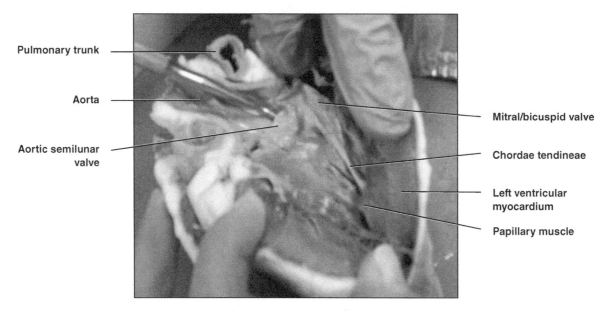

Pulmonary trunk
Aorta
Aortic semilunar valve

Mitral/bicuspid valve
Chordae tendineae
Left ventricular myocardium
Papillary muscle

Figure 3.24. Anterior View with Aorta Open

You have successfully opened the left side of the heart and followed the blood flow through this side of the heart.

Left & Right pulmonary veins → Left atrium → Left ventricle → Aorta

PART 3

BLOOD VESSELS

SECTION A – BLOOD VESSELS

Blood vessels are an important part of the cardiovascular system. They allow the transportation of the blood to and from the heart. There are three main types of blood vessels—arteries, capillaries, and veins. There are structural differences as well as functional differences between the different types of vessels. If you measure the entire length of all the blood vessels in the body—arteries, veins, and capillaries—it measures over 60,000 miles.

Arteries are the vessels that carry blood away from the heart. The largest artery in the body is the aorta. Its diameter is about the same as a garden hose. Arteries have muscular walls that can withstand the pressure the heart generates when pumping the blood. These vessels branch as they travel away from the heart, and the vessels become narrower and narrower. Small arteries are called arterioles.

Arteries have three layers to their walls. The outer layer is the tunica adventitia or externa. This layer is connective tissue that contains collagen and elastic fibers. The middle layer consists of smooth muscle and is called tunica media. It is this layer that controls the diameter of the vessel. The inner layer is called the tunica intima or interna. This is the endothelium that provides a smooth surface for blood to flow over and as a result helps prevent blood clotting.

Veins are vessels that carry blood toward the heart. They start out as small veins or venules that merge to form bigger vessels, the veins that continue to get bigger until all veins merge with the two largest veins in the body: the inferior and superior vena cava. Veins have the same three layers in their walls as arteries; however, the tunica media is a much thinner layer of smooth muscle. Veins do not carry blood under high pressure and one of their functions is to serve as a reservoir for blood. By having very little smooth muscle in their walls they are distensible. Unfortunately, the lack of smooth muscle inhibits the return of blood to the heart from gravity dependent areas. As a result the endothelium of veins contains semilunar valves to insure one way blood flow back toward the heart.

The smallest vessels are the **capillaries**. These vessels connect arterioles to venules. The walls of the capillaries are only one cell thick—simple squamous epithelium. All nutrient and waste exchange occurs through the walls of the capillaries.

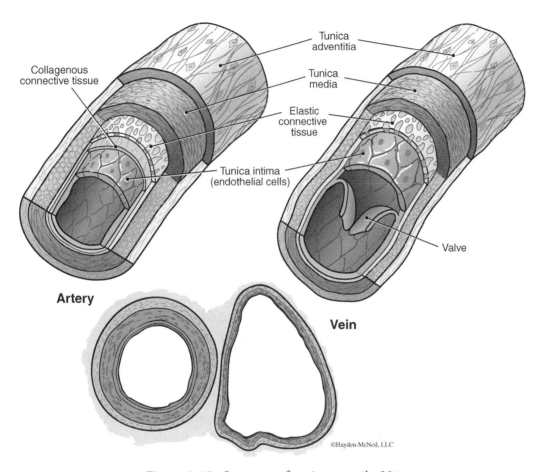

Figure 3.25. Structure of an Artery and a Vein

SECTION B – SYSTEMIC ARTERIES

There are two major pathways of blood vessels in the body: the pulmonary circulatory system and the systemic circulatory system. The pulmonary circuit is responsible for carrying the blood from the heart to the blood vessels of the lungs for oxygenation and then returning it to the heart. The pulmonary circulation leaves the right ventricle via the pulmonary trunk, which then divides into the right and left pulmonary arteries that carry the blood to the lungs. In the lungs the arteries run into arterioles which run into capillaries where the blood is oxygenated. The oxygenated blood leaves the capillaries by way of the venules which drain into veins and eventually lead to four pulmonary veins, two on the right and two on the left. The four pulmonary veins return the oxygenated blood to the left atrium.

The systemic circulatory system is responsible for delivering oxygenated blood from the heart to the tissues of the body and returning the deoxygenated blood to the heart. The blood leaves the left ventricle and travels out the aorta to the systemic arteries for delivery of nutrients and oxygen to all tissues of the body. The deoxygenated blood from the tissues is returned to the heart by the systemic veins via the superior and inferior vena cavae.

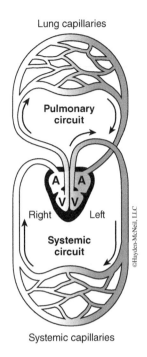

Figure 3.26. Pulmonary and Systemic Circulatory Systems

Aorta

The largest artery in the body is the **aorta** which leaves the left ventricle. As the aorta leaves the ventricle it is known as the **ascending aorta**. The aorta then makes a turn posteriorly to create the **aortic arch**; it then begins travelling down the back of the thoracic cavity as the **descending aorta**. All systemic arteries ultimately arise from the aorta.

Arteries of the Head, Neck, and Upper Extremities

The first arteries off the aorta are the **coronary arteries** that branch off the ascending aorta just superiorly to the aortic semilunar valve. The next arteries originate off the aortic arch. The first artery off the aortic arch is the **brachiocephalic** (BRAK-e-o-sah-FAL-ik) or **innominate artery** (INOM-inate). This artery gives rise to the arteries that supply blood to the tissues of the head and the right upper extremities. It divides into the **right common carotid artery** that supplies the right side of the head and neck and the **right subclavian artery** (sub-KLAY-ve-an) that supplies the right arm. The second artery off the aortic arch is the **left common carotid artery** (kah-ROT id) that supplies the left side of the head and neck. Placing your fingers on either side of the neck allows you to feel the pulse of the blood that is moving through the common carotid arteries. Anywhere you can feel a pulse is known as a **pulse point**. The third artery off the arch is the **left subclavian artery** that supplies the left arm.

The common carotids branch to give rise to the **external carotid arteries** and the **internal carotid arteries**. The external carotid arteries supply the upper neck, face, and scalp. The **facial artery** and the **superficial temporal artery** are both branches of the external carotid artery and are pulse points. The internal carotid arteries enter the skull and supply the brain and eyes.

The subclavian arteries are named because they pass under the clavicle. These arteries are continuous with the **axillary arteries** (AK-sah-LER-ee). Before the subclavian arteries become the axillary arteries they give rise to the **vertebral arteries**. The name changes from subclavian to axillary arteries at about the level of the first rib. The axillary arteries are then continuous with the **brachial arteries**, another pulse point. The axillary arteries pass through the axilla and emerge as the brachial arteries. The brachial arteries divide at the level of the elbow into the **radial** and **ulnar arteries**. The radial artery is the normal site used to take a pulse. The **deep palmar arch** is an anastomosis (an artery to artery connection) between the radial artery and the deep branch of the ulnar artery.

129

The vertebral arteries pass through the transverse foramen of the cervical vertebrae to enter the skull to supply the superior spinal cord and the brainstem. Once inside the skull the vertebral arteries anastomose with the internal carotid arteries to form the circle of Willis. This structure gives rise to all of the cerebral arteries.

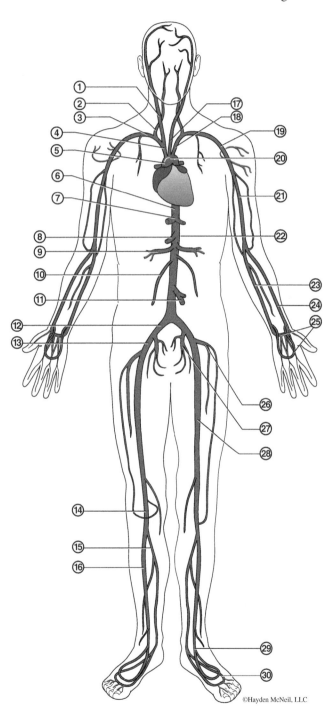

1. Right common carotid
2. Vertebral
3. Right subclavian
4. Brachiocephalic trunk/artery (innominate)
5. Ascending aorta
6. Descending aorta
7. Celiac trunk/artery
8. Superior mesenteric
9. Renal
10. Gonadal
11. Inferior mesenteric
12. Common iliac
13. External iliac
14. Popliteal
15. Posterior tibial
16. Anterior tibial
17. Left common carotid
18. Left subclavian
19. Axillary
20. Aortic arch
21. Brachial
22. Abdominal aorta
23. Ulnar
24. Radial
25. Deep palmar arches
26. Deep femoral
27. Internal iliac (hypogastric)
28. Femoral
29. Dorsalis pedis
30. Plantar arch

©Hayden McNeil, LLC

Figure 3.27. Systemic Arteries

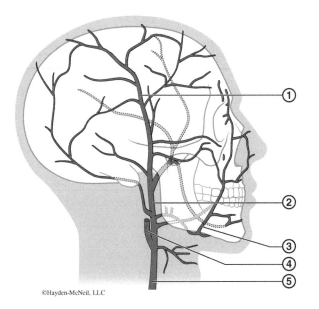

1. Superficial temporal a.
2. External carotid a.
3. Facial a.
4. Internal carotid a.
5. Common carotid a.

©Hayden-McNeil, LLC

Figure 3.28. Arteries of the Head

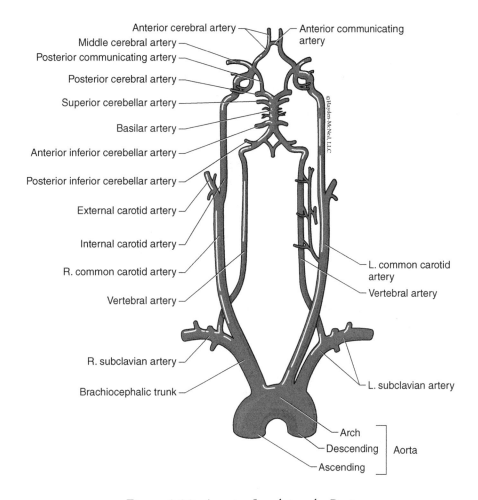

Anterior cerebral artery
Middle cerebral artery
Posterior communicating artery
Posterior cerebral artery
Superior cerebellar artery
Basilar artery
Anterior inferior cerebellar artery
Posterior inferior cerebellar artery
External carotid artery
Internal carotid artery
R. common carotid artery
Vertebral artery
R. subclavian artery
Brachiocephalic trunk

Anterior communicating artery

©Hayden-McNeil, LLC

L. common carotid artery
Vertebral artery
L. subclavian artery

Arch
Descending } Aorta
Ascending

Figure 3.29. Arteries Supplying the Brain

131

Table 3.6: Arteries of Head, Neck, and Upper Extremities

ARTERY	SOURCE	TISSUES SUPPLIED	ADDITIONAL INFORMATION
aorta, ascending	left ventricle of the heart	heart, entire body	continues as the aortic arch
aorta, descending	continuation of aortic arch	thoracic and abdominal organs	
aortic arch	continuation of the ascending aorta	the entire body except the heart	aortic arch continues as the descending aorta
axillary	continuation of subclavian artery	pectoral region, shoulder region, and upper limb	continuous with the brachial artery
brachial	continuation of the axillary artery	arm, forearm, and hand	
brachiocephalic trunk/ artery or innominate	aortic arch. 1st branch	right side of the head and neck; right upper limb and right side of the chest wall	there is only one brachiocephalic artery
carotid, common	brachiocephalic trunk (right), aortic arch (left)	most of the head and upper neck	
carotid, external	common carotid artery	upper neck, face, and scalp	
carotid, internal	common carotid artery	brain, eye and orbit, forehead	
deep palmar arch	radial and deep ulnar arteries	palm and fingers of each hand	
facial	external carotid artery	lower part of the palatine tonsil, submandibular gland, and the facial muscles	
radial	brachial artery	posterior elbow, posterior forearm, posterior hand, deep portion of palmar side of the hand, thumb	
subclavian	brachiocephalic trunk (right), aortic arch (left)	neck, brain, spinal cord, thyroid gland, larynx, shoulder, chest muscles, upper limb	continuous with the axillary artery
superficial temporal	External carotid artery	skin, muscles and mucosa of the upper lip and the lower part of the nasal septum	
ulnar	brachial artery	medial side of the anterior forearm, posterior forearm, superficial palm, fingers	
vertebral	subclavian artery	deep neck, spinal cord; medulla	

Arteries of the Abdomen and Lower Extremities

The descending aorta passes through the thoracic cavity and the diaphragm to enter the abdominal cavity. In the abdominal cavity there are several arteries that arise from the descending abdominal aorta. Branching off the sides of the aorta are the **renal arteries** that travel to the right and left kidney.

There are three arteries that arise from the aorta as single arteries rather than pairs as most arteries do. These three arteries branch from the anterior surface of the aorta: **celiac trunk** (SE-le-ak), **superior mesenteric artery** (MES-en-TER-ik) and **inferior mesenteric artery**. The celiac trunk gives rise to the gastric, splenic, and hepatic arteries. The superior and inferior mesenteric arteries branch to several parts of the intestinal tract.

As the aorta reaches the pelvic region at about the 4th lumbar vertebra it bifurcates or divides into the two **common iliac arteries**. The common iliac arteries then divide into the **internal iliac** or **hypogastric arteries** (IL-ee-ak) and the **external iliac arteries**. The internal iliac arteries supply organs in the pelvis and the hip and gluteal regions. The external iliac is continuous with the femoral artery and supplies the lower limb. As the external iliac arteries leave the pelvic region the name changes to the **femoral arteries** (FEM-or-al) that supply the lower limbs.

The femoral arteries, another pulse point, supply the tissues of the thigh. These arteries are continuous with the **popliteal arteries** (POP-lah-TE-al). As the femoral arteries pass through the thighs they course toward the back of the legs to pass behind the knees. At this point the name of the arteries changes from femoral to the popliteal arteries. The popliteal arteries supply the knees and the legs. These arteries then bifurcate into the **anterior** and **posterior tibial arteries**. The anterior tibial arteries supply the anterior surface of the legs and the top of the feet. The posterior tibial arteries supply the posterior surface of the legs and the soles of the feet. The **dorsalis pedis** (PEED-ahs), a branch of the anterior tibial artery, is used to determine perfusion of the foot.

Table 3.7: Arteries of Abdomen and Lower Extremities

Artery	Source	Tissues Supplied
anterior tibial	popliteal artery	anterior leg; dorsum of foot and deep foot
celiac trunk	abdominal aorta	stomach, lower esophagus, liver, upper duodenum, pancreas, spleen
common iliac	abdominal aorta	pelvis, lower limb
dorsalis pedis	anterior tibial artery	dorsal surface of the foot
external iliac	common iliac artery	lower limb
femoral	external iliac artery	thigh, leg, and foot
internal iliac	common iliac artery	pelvic viscera, gluteal region, hip, medial thigh
inferior mesenteric	abdominal aorta	splenic flexure, descending colon, sigmoid colon, superior part of rectum
popliteal	femoral artery	knee, leg, and foot
posterior tibial	popliteal artery	posterior and lateral leg, plantar aspect of the foot
renal	abdominal aorta	kidney, upper ureter, suprarenal gland
superior mesenteric	abdominal aorta	pancreas, distal duodenum, jejunum, ileum, part of colon

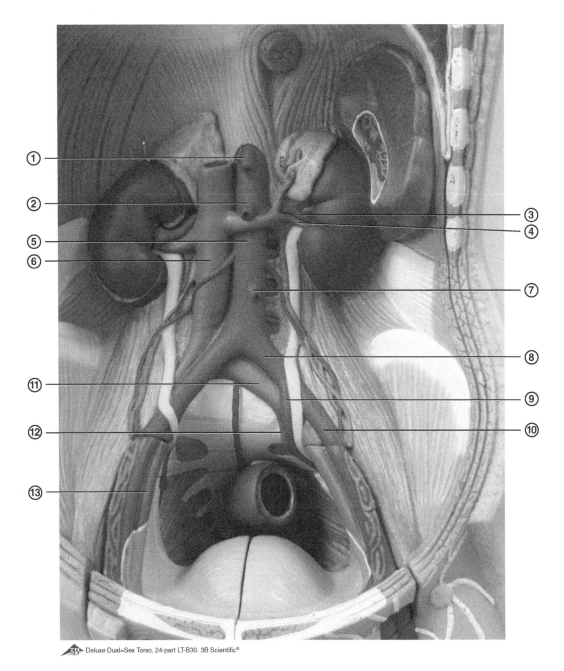

Deluxe Dual=Sex Torso, 24-part LT-B30, 3B Scientific®

1. Celiac trunk/artery
2. Superior mesenteric artery
3. Renal artery
4. Renal vein
5. Abdominal aorta
6. Inferior vena cava
7. Inferior mesenteric artery
8. Common iliac artery
9. Internal iliac/hypogastric artery
10. External iliac artery
11. Common iliac vein
12. Internal iliac/hypogastric vein
13. External iliac vein

Figure 3.30. Abdominal Blood Vessels

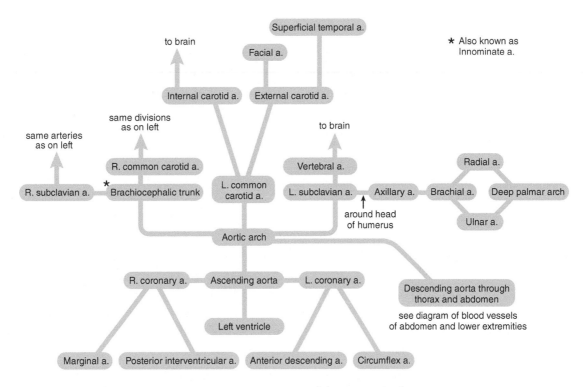

Figure 3.31. Arteries of the Upper Body

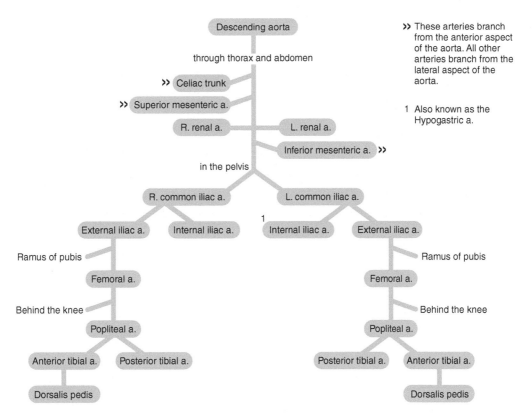

Figure 3.32. Arteries of the Lower Body

135

SECTION C – SYSTEMIC VEINS

The systemic veins are responsible for returning deoxygenated blood from the tissues to the right atrium. Whereas arteries branch and go from large to small, veins merge and go from small to large. The venous vessels begin with the venules off the capillary beds; these venules merge to form small veins and small veins join to form larger veins.

The largest veins in the body are the superior and inferior vena cavae. The **superior vena cava** drains the tissues of the head, neck, and upper extremities and the **inferior vena cava** drains all the tissues below the level of the heart. The heart tissue is drained by the coronary sinus.

The superior vena cava is formed by the fusion of the **right** and **left brachiocephalic** or **innominate veins**. The **internal jugular vein** and the **subclavian vein** merge to form each brachiocephalic vein. The internal jugular vein drains the brain tissues. The **external jugular vein** drains the tissues of the head and neck and empties into the subclavian vein.

The subclavian vein is a continuation of the **axillary vein**. The **cephalic vein** (sah-FAL-ik) empties into the subclavian vein. The cephalic vein, located on the lateral surface of the arm, drains the hand and the forearm. The axillary vein is formed by the fusion of the **brachial veins** and the **basilic vein** (bah-SIL-ik). There are two brachial veins, one on each side of the brachial artery. The basilic vein, found on the anterior medial surface of the arm, drains the hand and forearm. The **median cubital vein** (KU-bi-tal) is found in the bend of the elbow and drains into the basilic vein. This is the vein commonly used to obtain a blood draw by a phlebotomist.

The inferior vena cava is formed by the fusion of the **right** and **left common iliac veins**. In the thoracic regions there are two major veins that drain thoracic structures: the **azygos** (a-ZYE-gus) and **hemiazygos** veins. The **azygos vein** is a large vein that drains into the superior vena cava just before it enters the pericardial sac. It can be found on the right anterior surface of the vertebral column. The **hemiazygos vein** is found on the left anterior surface of the vertebral column. It is almost the equivalent of the azygos vein but it does not rise as high in the thorax as the azygos vein and it drains into the azygos.

In the abdominal region most of the veins from the tissues drain into the inferior vena cava. The **renal veins** that drain the tissues of the kidneys and the **hepatic veins** that drain the liver enter the inferior vena cava. The veins in the abdomen that do not drain into the inferior vena cava are the veins that drain into the hepatic portal system. This system is discussed in the next section.

The **external iliac veins** and the **internal iliac** or **hypogastric veins** merge to form the common iliac veins. The internal iliac vein arises in the pelvic region and the external iliac vein is a continuation of the **femoral vein** from the thigh.

In the thigh the **great saphenous vein** (sah-FE-nus), the longest vein in the body, joins the femoral vein just before it changes names to the external iliac vein. The great saphenous vein originates on the medial surface of the foot and extends to the groin area. The femoral vein is a continuation of the **popliteal vein**. The popliteal vein is formed by the fusion of the **anterior** and **posterior tibial vein** in the upper leg.

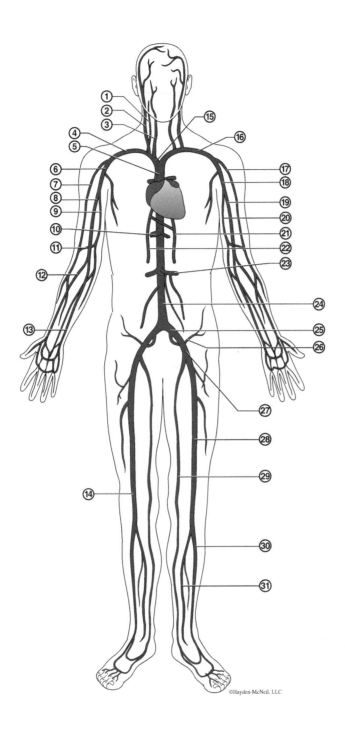

1. Vertebral
2. External jugular
3. Internal jugular
4. R. subclavian
5. Superior vena cava
6. R. axillary
7. R. cephalic
8. R. brachial
9. R. basilic
10. Hepatic
11. Median cubital
12. Radial
13. Ulnar
14. Popliteal
15. R. brachiocephalic
16. L. subclavian
17. L. cephalic
18. L. axillary
19. L. brachial
20. L. basilic
21. Hemiazygos
22. Azygos
23. Renal
24. Inferior vena cava
25. L. common iliac
26. Internal iliac (hypogastric)
27. External iliac
28. Femoral
29. Great saphenous
30. Anterior tibial
31. Posterior tibial

©Hayden-McNeil, LLC

Figure 3.33. Systemic Veins

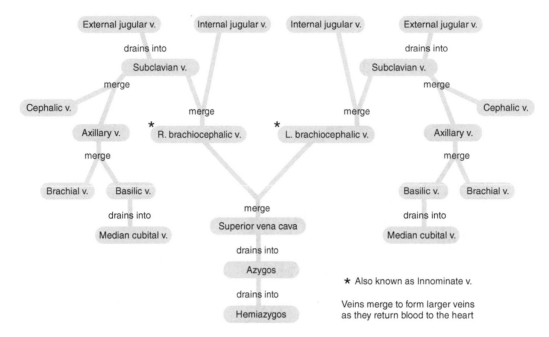

Figure 3.34. Veins of the Upper Body

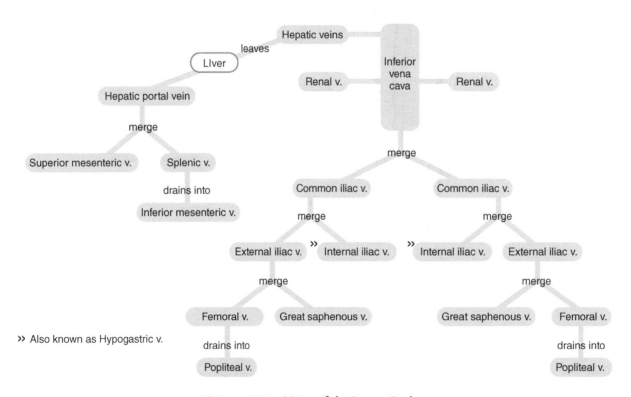

Figure 3.35. Veins of the Lower Body

Hint: The veins are easier to learn after you learn the arteries. Most veins have the same name as the artery the vein sits next to.

SECTION D – HEPATIC PORTAL SYSTEM

Most of the veins of the abdominal organs empty into the inferior vena cava. However, the veins leaving the digestive system first pass through the liver for processing by way of the hepatic portal system. The liver is capable of removing and storing some nutrients as well as detoxifying harmful substances that may be present in the blood. The blood from the digestive system is delivered to the liver by the **hepatic portal** (sometimes just **portal**) **vein**.

The hepatic portal vein is formed by the union of the **splenic vein** and **superior mesenteric vein**. The splenic vein drains the spleen, the pancreas, by way of several small **pancreatic veins**, and part of the stomach. The superior mesenteric vein drains the small intestine as well as the ascending and transverse colon. The **inferior mesenteric vein** receives blood from the distal colon and drains into the splenic vein. The **gastric veins** drain the stomach and empty directly into the hepatic portal vein.

After the blood is processed in the liver it is returned to the systemic venous system by the **hepatic veins** that exit the liver on the superior surface and drain into the inferior vena cava.

Hepatic Portal System

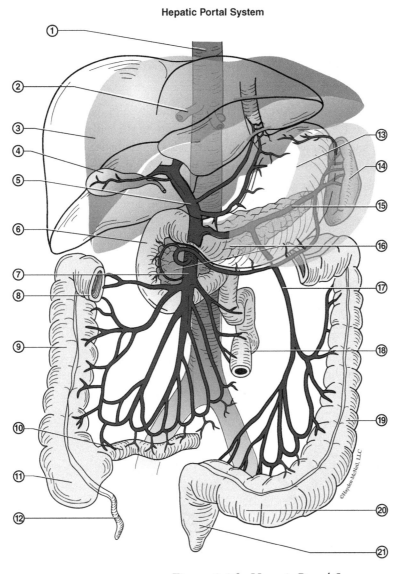

1. Inferior vena cava
2. Hepatic vein
3. Liver
4. Gallbladder
5. Hepatic portal vein
6. Duodenum
7. Superior mesenteric vein
8. Transverse colon (cut)
9. Ascending colon
10. Ileum (cut)
11. Cecum
12. Appendix
13. Stomach
14. Spleen
15. Splenic vein
16. Pancreas
17. Inferior mesenteric vein
18. Ileum (cut)
19. Descending colon
20. Sigmoid colon
21. Rectum

Figure 3.36. Hepatic Portal System

SECTION E – BLOOD PRESSURE

When the heart contracts it pushes blood out of the heart into the arteries. This will exert a pressure on the walls of the arteries. The pressure that is exerted during the contraction of the heart is known as the **systolic pressure** (sis-TOL-ik). When the heart is relaxed the pressure within the arteries drops to a lower pressure known as the **diastolic pressure** (di-a-STOL-ik).

The values of the systolic and diastolic pressures provide important clinical information. There are different ways to measure this pressure, invasive and noninvasive. In most clinical settings noninvasive methods are used. The simplest and most accurate noninvasive technique is to use a sphygmomanometer or a blood pressure cuff.

To measure an individual's blood pressure ideally the individual should be sitting with his/her feet flat on the floor and his/her back supported. The arm should be supported at the level of the heart and the individual should be allowed to sit quietly for about 5 minutes before the measurement is taken.

The cuff should properly fit the individual. Most cuffs have an index marking to indicate if the cuff is too small. The cuff should be placed snugly around the arm but not too tightly. The stethoscope is placed over the brachial artery. The release valve on the bulb must be closed for the cuff to inflate but it should not be closed so tightly that it cannot be released with a couple of fingers during the measurement.

The cuff will be inflated to about 30 mm Hg above the expected systolic blood pressure. This is done by rapidly squeezing the bulb on the cuff. This pressure will occlude the artery.

The air is slowly released from the cuff, a couple of mm Hg at a time, while listening with the stethoscope. The gauge attached to the cuff is monitored as the cuff is deflated. As the pressure in the cuff matches the pressure in the artery, the artery will begin to open and blood will start flowing through a partially occluded artery. This causes sounds known as Korotkoff sounds to be heard by the stethoscope. The pressure on the gauge is noted when the first sound is heard. This is the systolic pressure. The pressure in the cuff continues to be released until the artery is no longer partially occluded, this will cause the Korotkoff sounds to disappear. The pressure is noted when the sounds disappear and this is the diastolic pressure.

Table 3.8: Blood Pressure Values

BLOOD PRESSURE	NORMAL	PREHYPERTENSION	HYPERTENSION
Systolic pressure (mm Hg)	< 120	120–139	> 140
Diastolic pressure (mm Hg)	< 80	80–89	> 90

Hypertension is not diagnosed based on one blood pressure measurement. The blood pressure should be measured over a few visits to the physician's office.

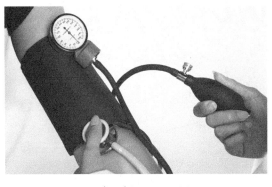

Figure 3.37. Blood Pressure Measurement

PART 4

LYMPHATICS

The lymphatics function to collect interstitial fluid and proteins to return it to the blood vessels as well as transporting digested fats from the small intestines to the bloodstream. Lymphatic tissues include the lymph nodes, tonsils, thymus, and spleen. The lymph nodes filter out foreign material and organisms in the lymph and are a site for lymphocytes to mature. This assists in fighting infections. All lymphatic tissues play a role in defending the body against infection.

Lymph in the interstitial fluid is drained by the **lymphatic vessels**. Lymphatic vessels are present in any tissues that have capillary beds. Tissues that are avascular do not require lymphatic vessels. The lymphatic vessels merge into large lymphatic vessels which eventually empty into one of two collecting ducts: the **right lymphatic duct** and the **thoracic duct**. The right lymphatic duct drains the right side of the body above the diaphragm and empties into the right subclavian vein. The thoracic duct is larger than the right lymphatic duct. It is located alongside the aorta. This duct collects the lymph from all lymphatic vessels below the diaphragm and the left side of the body above the diaphragm. It empties into the left subclavian vein. This returns the lymph fluid to the bloodstream. At the base of the thoracic duct is a sac-like structure known as the **cisterna chyli** (sis-TER-nah KYE-lee). This is the origin of the thoracic duct. The lacteals of the villi of the small intestine drain into this structure.

Located along the lymphatic vessels are **lymph nodes**. The nodes tend to be clustered in groups or chains along the vessels. The major clusters are the **cervical lymph nodes**, **axillary lymph nodes**, **inguinal lymph nodes** (ING-gwah-nal) as well as the nodes found in the thoracic, abdominal, and pelvic cavities.

The tonsils are lymphoid tissues located in the nasopharynx and oropharynx. They are part of the defense mechanism by trapping microorganisms that may enter the body through the nose or mouth.

The **thymus gland** is located in the mediastinum superior to the heart. It is largest in childhood and begins to shrink after puberty. Thymosins are hormones released by this gland. These hormones stimulate the maturation of the T lymphocytes.

The **spleen** is the largest lymphatic organ. It is located under the diaphragm on the left side of the abdomen. It filters blood to remove foreign particles, damaged red blood cells, and other material from the blood.

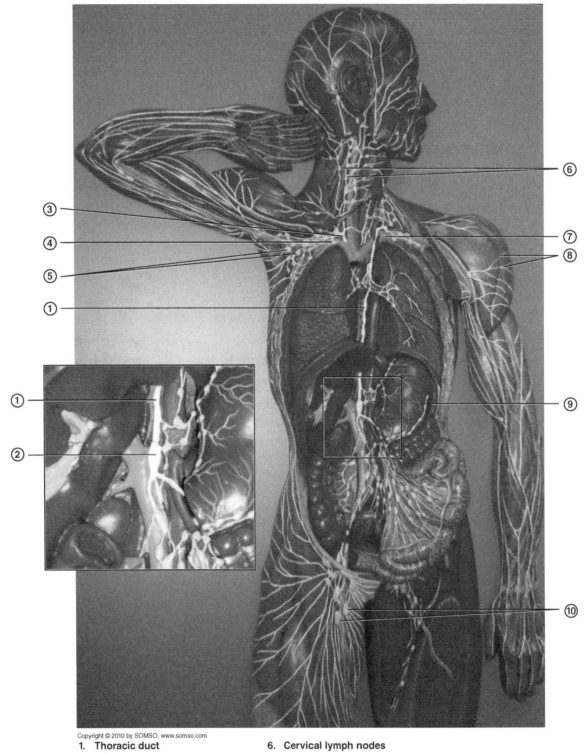

Copyright © 2010 by SOMSO, www.somso.com

1. Thoracic duct
2. Cisterna chyli
3. Right lymphatic duct
4. Right subclavian vein
5. Axillary lymph nodes
6. Cervical lymph nodes
7. Left subclavian vein
8. Lymphatic vessels
9. Spleen
10. Inguinal lymph nodes

Figure 3.38. Lymphatic System

Part 5

Respiratory System

The respiratory system is responsible for moving air in and out of the lungs. It is also involved in the exchange of oxygen and carbon dioxide between the alveoli (air sacs) in the lungs and the blood in the capillaries of the lungs.

Section A – Anatomy of the Respiratory System

The respiratory system can be divided into the upper respiratory tract and the lower respiratory tract. The upper respiratory tract consists of the nose, pharynx, and larynx. It is responsible for warming, filtering, and humidifying the inhaled air.

The nose is the structure best suited for warming, filtering, and humidifying the inhaled air. Air enters the nose through the **nares**, the opening to the **nasal cavity**. In the cavity are the **nasal conchae**, bony protuberances that increase the surface area in the nasal cavity. This allows the air to have more contact with the nasal mucosa.

Air can also enter the respiratory system through the mouth. The air will enter the **oral cavity** through the lips. The area between the lips and teeth is the **oral vestibule**. In the oral cavity proper the lateral boundaries are formed by the cheeks. The floor of the oral cavity is occupied by the **tongue**. The roof of the oral cavity is the palate. The palate consists of the bony **hard palate** anteriorly and the **soft palate** posteriorly. The **uvula** (U-vu-lah) is the portion of the soft palate that extends downward and can be seen in the back of the oral cavity.

The air leaves the nasal cavity and enters the pharynx. This is commonly referred to as "the throat." The pharynx can be subdivided into three regions. The **nasopharynx** (NAY-zo-FAR-ingks) is the region behind the nose. The **oropharynx** (O-ro-FAR-ingks) is the region behind the oral cavity. Finally, the **laryngopharynx** (lah-RING-go-FAR-ingks) is the region behind the larynx. The three different tonsils are found in the pharynx. On the posterior wall of the nasopharynx behind the uvula are the **pharyngeal tonsils**. This is lymphoid tissue that is known as the **adenoids** (AD-ah-noyds) when they are inflamed. The **aperature to the auditory (Eustachian) tube** is found in the nasopharynx as well. This is the structure that allows for the equalization of pressure in the middle ear. On the lateral walls of the oropharynx are the **palatine tonsils**. This is the lymphoid tissue that is commonly known as "the tonsils" and is removed in a tonsillectomy. At the root of the tongue are the **lingual tonsils** (LING-gwal). This tissue is removed along with the palatine tonsils during a tonsillectomy.

After leaving the pharynx the air enters the **larynx**. This is a cartilaginous structure located between the root of the tongue and the trachea that is known as the "voice box." The function of the larynx is to allow air to pass to the trachea. The larynx contains a cartilage that serves to protect the airway from foreign objects and it contains the **vocal cords** as well. There are several cartilages that make up the larynx, most of which are hyaline cartilage. The **epiglottis** is elastic cartilage rather than hyaline. It is a flexible cartilage located at the superior border of the larynx. It functions to close off the larynx during swallowing to prevent food from entering the airways or the lung.

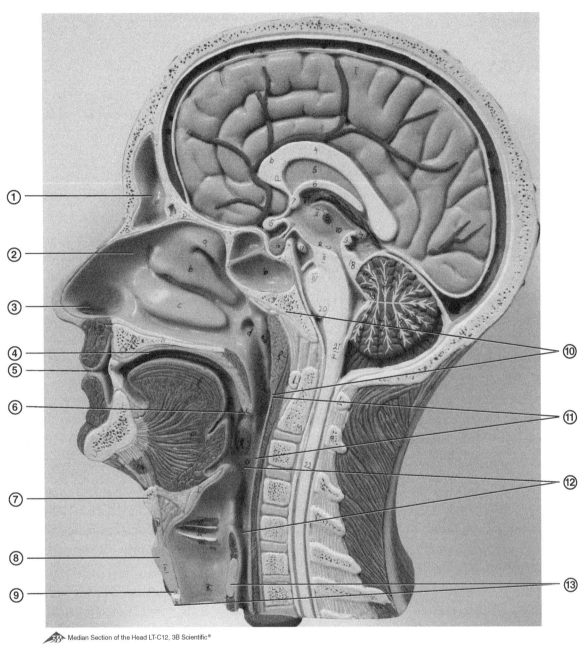

Median Section of the Head LT-C12, 3B Scientific®

1. Frontal sinus
2. Nasal cavity
3. Nares
4. Oral cavity
5. Oral vestibule
6. Uvula
7. Hyoid
8. Thyroid cartilage
9. Cricothyroid membrane/ligament
10. Nasopharynx
11. Oropharynx
12. Laryngopharynx
13. Cricoid cartilage

Figure 3.39. Nasal and Oral Cavity

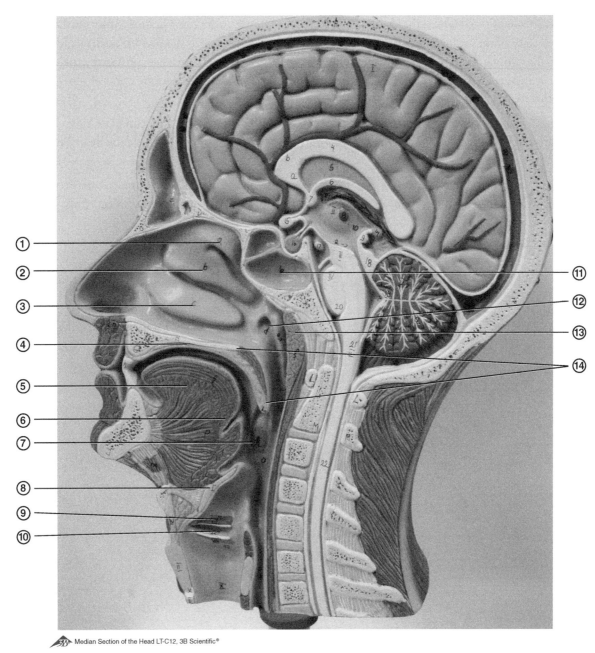

Median Section of the Head LT-C12, 3B Scientific®

1. Superior concha
2. Middle concha
3. Inferior concha
4. Hard palate
5. Tongue
6. Lingual tonsil
7. Palatine tonsil
8. Epiglottis
9. Vestibular folds
10. Vocal folds
11. Sphenoid sinus
12. Auditory tube aperature
13. Pharyngeal tonsil
14. Soft palate (uvula at tip)

Figure 3.40. Upper Respiratory Tract

The largest cartilage of the larynx is the **thyroid cartilage** also known as the Adam's apple. It forms the majority of the anterior surface of the larynx. The thyroid glands are located just inferior to the thyroid cartilage. It is connected superiorly to the hyoid bone by the thyrohyoid membrane and inferiorly to the cricoid cartilage by the **cricothyroid membrane**, or **ligament**. This membrane allows emergency entry into the airway in the event of obstruction of the airway superior to this point.

The lower border of the larynx is the **cricoid cartilage** (KRY-koyd). This is the only complete ring of cartilage in the respiratory tract. The cartilage is larger in the back and smaller in the front. It is frequently described as a reverse signet ring.

The **arytenoid cartilages** (ah-RIT-ahn-oid) are two pyramid-shaped cartilages above the cricoid cartilage on the posterior surface of the larynx. These movable cartilages function in the movement of the vocal cords.

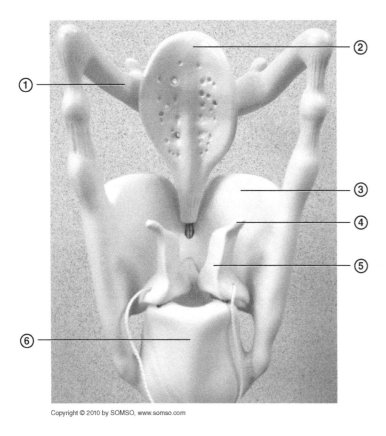

1. Hyoid bone
2. Epiglottis
3. Thyroid cartilage
4. Corniculate cartilage
5. Arytenoid cartilage
6. Cricoid cartilage

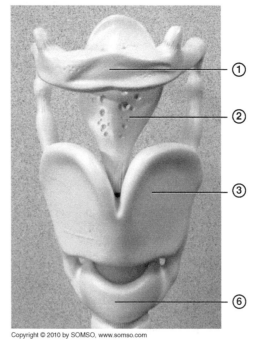

Figure 3.41. Larynx

When observing the larynx from above the vestibular folds, vocal folds and the opening between the vocal folds can be observed. Between the vocal folds there is a triangular opening. This is the **rima glottidis** (RYE-ma GLOT-ah-dis) an opening between vocal folds that allows air to enter the lower respiratory tract and the production of the voice. The vocal folds and the opening (rima glottidis) together form the **glottis**.

Posterior

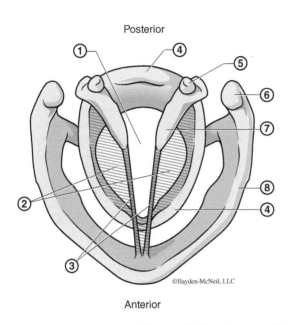

1. Rima glottidis
2. Vestibular folds
3. Vocal ligaments
4. Cricoid cartilage
5. Corniculate cartilage
6. Superior horn of thyroid cartilage
7. Arytenoid cartilage
8. Thyroid cartilage

©Hayden-McNeil, LLC

Anterior

Figure 3.42. Superior View of the Larynx

The next structure in the respiratory tract is the **trachea**. This is the first structure of the lower respiratory tract. The structures of the lower respiratory tract conduct the humidified, filtered, warmed air to the alveoli (air sacs) to participate in gas exchange. The trachea extends from the lower border of the larynx to the point it divides into the two primary bronchi. The trachea is supported by C-shaped cartilage rings. It shares its soft tissue posterior wall with the anterior wall of the **esophagus**. This allows the esophagus to expand to allow the passage of food.

The trachea divides into the **right** and **left bronchi** (singular bronchus) that enter the lungs. The end of the trachea where the division into the bronchi occurs is the **carina** (kah-RYE-nah). Each **bronchus** (BRONG-kus) divides multiple times as it extends into each lung. The diameter of a bronchus decreases with each division. As a bronchus becomes smaller and smaller the name changes from a bronchus to a **bronchiole** (BRONG-kee-ol). These airways are less than 1 mm in diameter. The bronchioles conduct the air into the region of the lung involved in gas exchange.

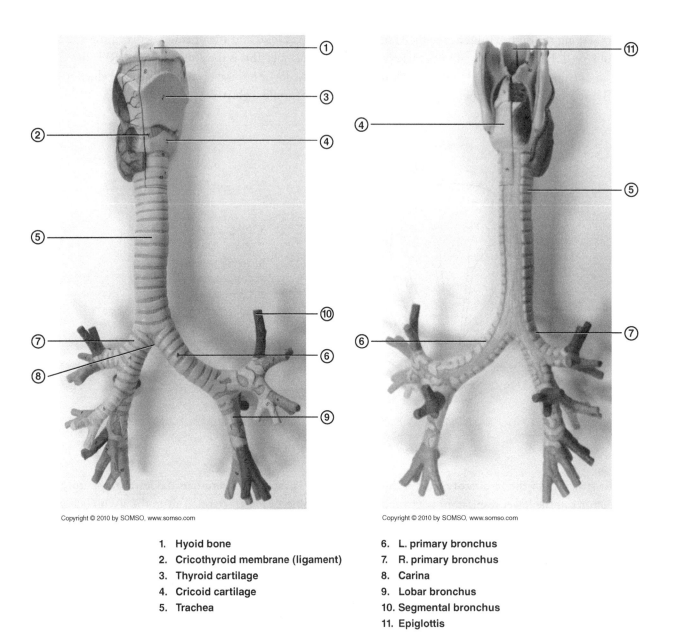

1. Hyoid bone
2. Cricothyroid membrane (ligament)
3. Thyroid cartilage
4. Cricoid cartilage
5. Trachea
6. L. primary bronchus
7. R. primary bronchus
8. Carina
9. Lobar bronchus
10. Segmental bronchus
11. Epiglottis

Figure 3.43. Trachea and Bronchial Tree

The **alveoli** (al-VE-o-lie) (singular **alveolus**) consist of several alveolar sacs that work together as a unit to participate in gas exchange. The structure of the alveoli is such that surface area is increased to allow for the maximum diffusion of oxygen and carbon dioxide. When observing the alveolar sacs, which are thin wall structures, you will note capillaries in close proximity. This is the ideal arrangement for diffusion. The wall of the alveolar sac is only one cell thick, the wall of the capillary is only one cell thick and they are only separated by a small interstitial space. This is a short distance that the oxygen and carbon dioxide can easily traverse.

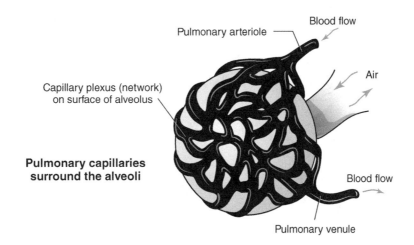

Figure 3.44. Conducting Airways and Alveoli

The lungs are located in the thoracic cavity. The area between the two lungs is the **mediastinum**. The bronchi, arteries, veins, lymphatics, and nerves enter and exit each lung on the medial surface at the **hilum**. The lungs are covered with a double-layered serous membrane called the pleura. The layer attached to the lung tissue is the **visceral pleura**; the layer lining the chest wall is the **parietal pleura**. There is a very small fluid-filled space between the two pleura that is the **pleural cavity**. It functions to prevent friction during breathing. The fluid creates a suction effect that keeps the lungs inflated. If something like a knife penetrates the chest wall and allows air to enter the pleural cavity, the lung will collapse. This is known as a pneumothorax.

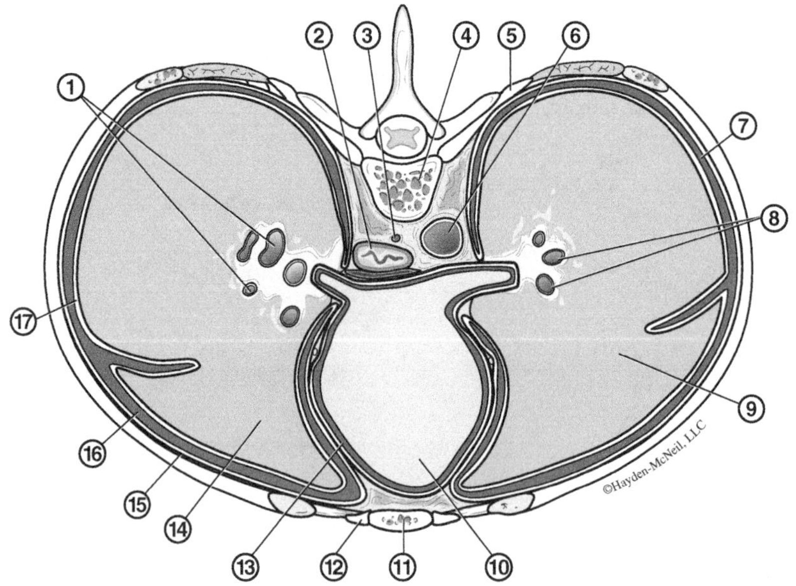

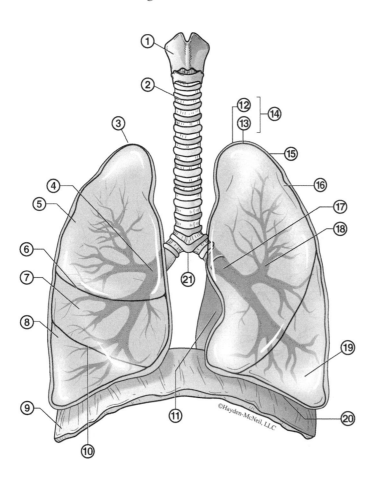

1. Branches of right bronchi
2. Esophagus
3. Thoracic duct
4. 8th thoracic vertebra
5. 8th rib
6. Descending aorta
7. Left pleural cavity
8. Branches of left bronchi
9. Left lung
10. Heart
11. Sternum
12. 5th right costal cartilage
13. Pericardial cavity
14. Right lung
15. Parietal pleura
16. Right pleural cavity
17. Visceral pleura

Figure 3.45. Transverse Section of Thoracic Cavity

1. Larynx
2. Trachea
3. Apex of lung
4. Right primary bronchus
5. Right upper lobe
6. Horizontal fissure
7. Right middle lobe
8. Right lower lobe
9. Diaphragm
10. Oblique fissure
11. Cardiac notch
12. Parietal pleura
13. Visceral pleura
14. Pleural membranes
15. Pleural cavity
16. Left upper lobe
17. Left primary bronchus
18. Secondary bronchus
19. Left lower lobe
20. Base of lung
21. Carina

Figure 3.46. Frontal View of Airways and Lungs

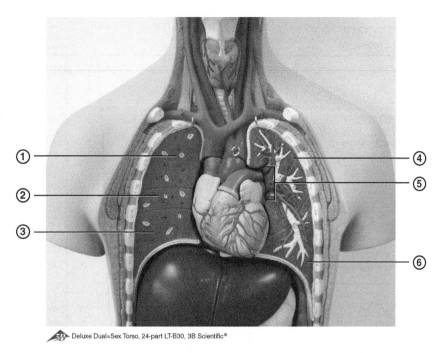

1. Right upper lobe
2. Right middle lobe
3. Right lower lobe
4. Left upper lobe
5. Hilum
6. Left lower lobe

Deluxe Dual=Sex Torso, 24-part LT-B30, 3B Scientific®

Figure 3.47. Anterior View of Lung

The lungs are divided into lobes by fissures. There are 2 lobes on the left and 3 lobes on the right. The **horizontal fissure** of the right lung is the cleft or crevice that separates the **upper lobe** from the **middle lobe** of that lung. The **oblique fissure** is the cleft that separates the right middle lobe from the right **lower lobe** or the left upper lobe from the left lower lobe.

SECTION B – PULMONARY VOLUMES

When evaluating an individual's lung function it is beneficial to look at the amount of air that can be moved under different conditions. An instrument that allows the measurement of these pulmonary volumes is a **spirometer**.

Tidal volume is the normal amount of air moved in or out of the lungs during a normal breath.

Expiratory reserve volume is the amount of air that can be exhaled after a normal expiration.

Inspiratory reserve volume is the amount of air that can be inhaled after a normal inspiration.

Residual volume is the amount of air left in the lungs after a maximal expiration.

Functional residual capacity is the amount of air left in the lungs after a normal expiration.

Vital capacity is the amount of air that can be maximally expired after a maximal inspiration.

Total lung capacity is the maximum amount of air that the lungs can hold.

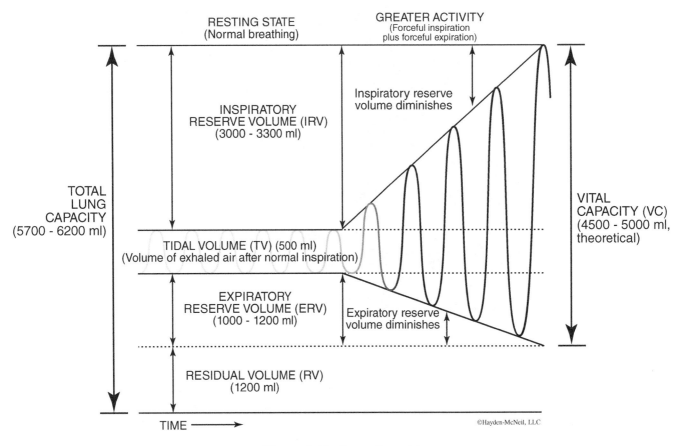

Figure 3.48. Lung Capacities

UNIT 4

DIGESTIVE SYSTEM, URINARY SYSTEM, REPRODUCTIVE SYSTEMS

This unit covers the final systems of the course which are the digestive, urinary, female and male reproductive systems. The digestive system is responsible for the breakdown and absorption of nutrients. The urinary system rids the body of waste and the reproductive systems produce the gametes (egg and sperm) to allow for reproduction.

DIGESTIVE TRACT

The digestive tract is also known as the gastrointestinal (GI) tract or the alimentary tract. It extends from the mouth to the anus. The liver, gallbladder, and pancreas support digestion.

Mouth

Food enters the digestive system through the mouth. In the mouth the food is torn apart by the teeth and mixed with saliva by the tongue to create a bolus of food to be swallowed. The saliva in the mouth is produced by 3 different pairs of salivary glands. The largest of the salivary glands are the **parotid glands** (PAHROT-id). They are located in the subcutaneous tissue anterior and inferior to the ears. The **submandibular glands** are located in the subcutaneous tissue beneath the rami of the mandibles. These glands produce the majority of the saliva. The last of the salivary glands are the **sublingual glands**, which are located beneath the tongue. These glands produce the least amount of saliva. After the food is mixed with saliva it is swallowed and passes through the oropharynx to the esophagus.

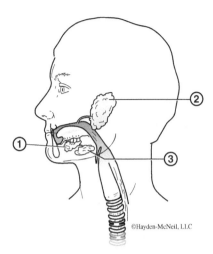

1. Sublingual salivary gland
2. Parotid salivary gland
3. Submandibular salivary gland

©Hayden-McNeil, LLC

Figure 4.1. Salivary Glands

Esophagus

The **esophagus** (ESOF-ahgus) extends from the laryngopharynx through the diaphragm to the stomach. This is a muscular tube; the upper third is skeletal muscle and the remainder is smooth muscle. Food is moved down the esophagus by peristaltic waves.

Stomach

The **stomach** is located beneath the diaphragm on the left side of the abdomen. It is between the esophagus and the duodenum on the small intestine. It is a hollow smooth-muscle organ that is sometimes described as J-shaped. The stomach mixes the food with gastric juice by segmentation to create chyme. It begins protein digestion by denaturing the proteins and pepsin's action on peptide bonds. The stomach is able to absorb a small amount of some substances. It also moves the chyme into the small intestine by peristalsis.

The stomach has three parts: the fundus, the body, and the pylorus. The **fundus** (FUN-dus) of the stomach is the upper portion of the stomach that extends superior to the esophageal opening of the stomach. The **body** is the central region of the stomach. The **pylorus** (PIELOR-us) is the region that narrows as it approaches the opening to the small intestine.

Both openings in the stomach are controlled by a **sphincter** (SFINGK-tur). This is a circular band of smooth muscle that can restrict or allow the passage of food in and out of the stomach. At the junction of the esophagus and the stomach is the **lower esophageal** or **cardiac sphincter**. This sphincter prevents the food and stomach acid from flowing back into the esophagus. At the opening of the stomach in the duodenum of the small intestine is the **pyloric sphincter**. This controls the amount of chyme entering the duodenum for digestion. It usually only allows about a teaspoon of chyme at a time to enter the small intestine.

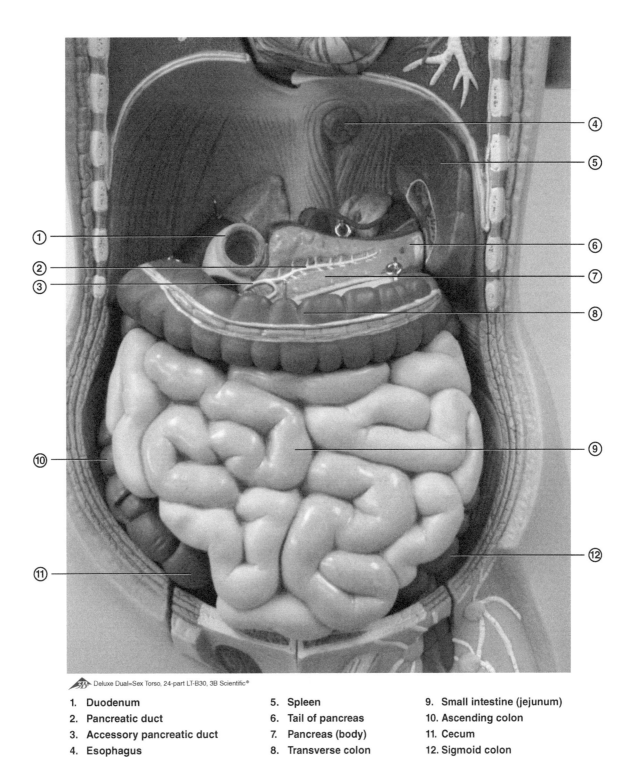

Deluxe Dual=Sex Torso, 24-part LT-B30, 3B Scientific®

1. Duodenum
2. Pancreatic duct
3. Accessory pancreatic duct
4. Esophagus

5. Spleen
6. Tail of pancreas
7. Pancreas (body)
8. Transverse colon

9. Small intestine (jejunum)
10. Ascending colon
11. Cecum
12. Sigmoid colon

Figure 4.2. Organs of Abdominal Cavity with Liver and Stomach Removed

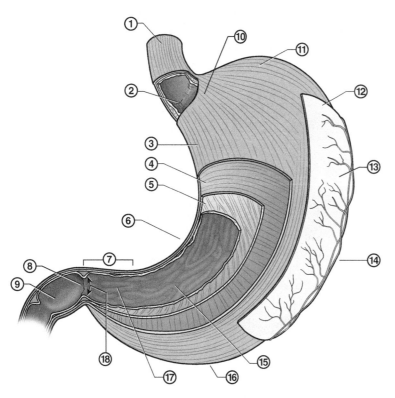

Stomach, anterior view

1. Esophagus
2. Lower esophageal sphincter
3. Longitudinal muscle layer
4. Circular muscle layer
5. Oblique muscle layer overlying gastric mucosa
6. Lesser curvature (medial surface)
7. Pylorus
8. Pyloric opening
9. Duodenum
10. Cardiac zone
11. Fundus of stomach
12. Visceral peritoneum (serosa)
13. Body of stomach
14. Greater curvature (lateral surface)
15. Rugae
16. Antrum of stomach
17. Pyloric antrum
18. Pyloric sphincter (composed mainly of thickened circular muscle)

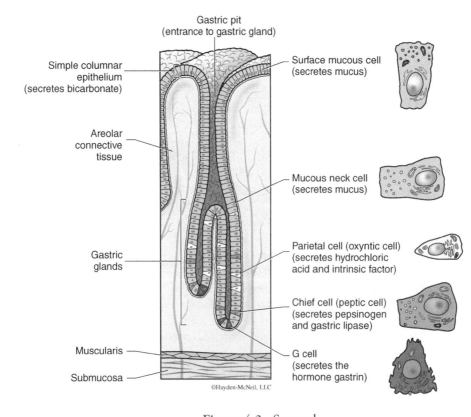

©Hayden-McNeil, LLC

Figure 4.3. Stomach

Small Intestine

The **small intestine** extends from the stomach to the large intestine. It is called the small intestine because it is smaller in diameter than the large intestine; however, the small intestine is much longer than the large intestine. The small intestine completes the digestion and absorption of the nutrients. To assist in this function the small intestine receives secretions from the pancreas, liver, and gallbladder. The small intestine also moves the waste products into the large intestine.

There are 3 parts to the small intestine: the duodenum, the jejunum and the ileum. The **duodenum** (DOO-ahdee-num or doo-OD-inum) is the initial section of the small intestine. It is the location of the pancreatic duct and common bile duct openings. These ducts carry the pancreatic juice and bile to the duodenum so it can continue with the digestion of chyme. Bile allows the emulsification of fat so that it can be digested and pancreatic juice contains enzymes. The point at which the common bile duct and pancreatic duct meet there is a dilation which is the **ampulla of Vater** (am-PYU-lah FAT-er) or the **hepatopancreatic ampulla**. It opens into the duodenum inferiorly to the accessory pancreatic duct at the major duodenal papilla. The duodenum continues with the digestion of chyme as well as some absorption of nutrients. The majority of digestion occurs in the duodenum.

The middle section of the small intestine is the **jejunum** (JIJOO-num). Digestion is completed in the jejunum. The final section of the small intestine is the **ileum** (IL-ee-um). Its main function is absorption. There is a valve between the ileum and the large intestine, the **ileocecal valve** (IL-ee-OSEE-kahl), to prevent the backflow of waste material into the small intestine.

The small intestine mucosa consists of finger-like projections known as **villi** (singular **villus** (VIL-us)) that increase the surface area available for absorption. In the core of each villus is a **capillary bed**, a **lacteal** (LAK-tee-ahl), and nerves. The lacteal is a lymphatic vessel that carries the chylomicrons away from the small intestine.

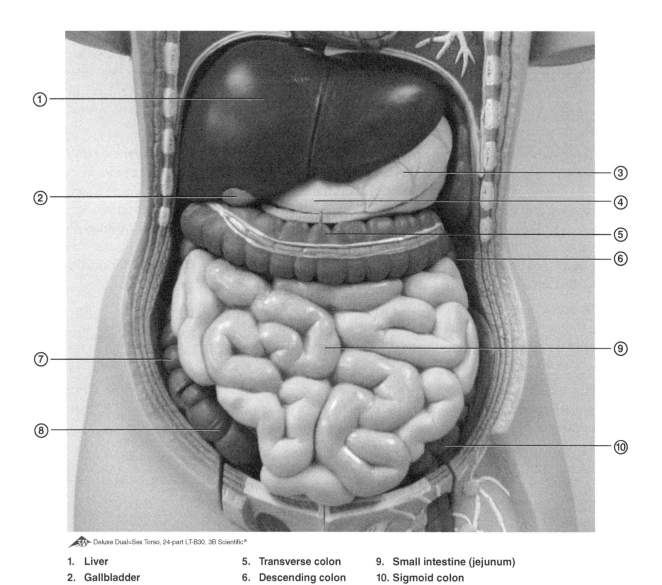

Deluxe Dual=Sex Torso, 24-part LT-B30, 3B Scientific®

1. Liver
2. Gallbladder
3. Stomach (body)
4. Pyloric region of stomach

5. Transverse colon
6. Descending colon
7. Ascending colon
8. Cecum

9. Small intestine (jejunum)
10. Sigmoid colon

Figure 4.4. Abdominal Organs

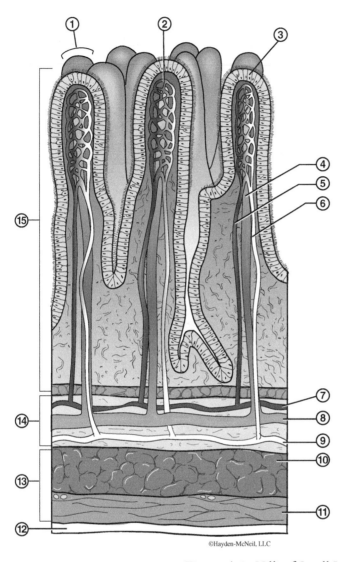

1. Villus
2. Capillary bed
3. Simple columnar epithelium
4. Lacteal
5. Arteriole
6. Venule
7. Artery
8. Lymph duct
9. Vein
10. Circular layer of muscle
11. Longitudinal layer of muscle
12. Serosa
13. Muscularis
14. Submucosa
15. Mucosa

©Hayden-McNeil, LLC

Figure 4.5. Villi of Small Intestine

Large Intestine

The large intestine, also known as the colon, extends from the small intestine to the anal canal. The large intestine prepares the watery waste material from the small intestine for excretion as feces. In doing so the colon reabsorbs water, some minerals, and some vitamins produced by colonic bacteria. There are seven parts to the large intestine: cecum, appendix, ascending colon, transverse colon, descending colon, sigmoid colon, and rectum. The **cecum** (SEE-cum) is a blind-end pouch that receives the waste material from the ileum through the ileocecal valve. The **appendix** is located on the posteroinferior aspect of the cecum.

The cecum leads into the **ascending colon**, which projects upward on the right side of the abdomen to just below the liver. It bends to the left at the hepatic flexure to become the **transverse colon**. The transverse colon spans the abdomen cavity until near the spleen where it bends inferiorly at the splenic flexure to become the **descending colon**. The descending colon travels down the left side of the abdomen. In the lower left quadrant at the edge of the pelvis the descending colon bends into an S-shaped curve known as the **sigmoid colon**. The sigmoid colon ends at the **rectum**. The rectum serves as a storage site for fecal material until defecation.

The rectum becomes the **anal canal** which ends with the **anus**, the opening to the exterior of the body. The anus has two sphincters to control the movement of fecal material. The first is the **interior anal sphincter** which is smooth muscle and involuntary. The second is the **external anal sphincter** which is skeletal muscle and usually is under voluntary control.

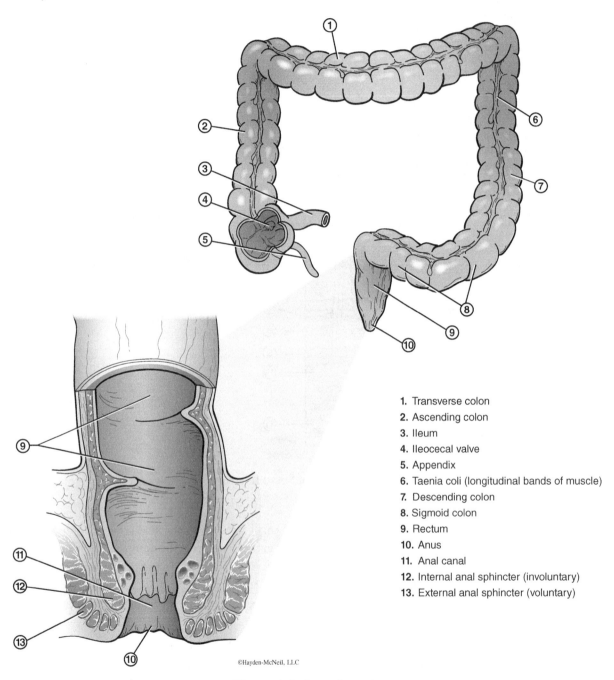

1. Transverse colon
2. Ascending colon
3. Ileum
4. Ileocecal valve
5. Appendix
6. Taenia coli (longitudinal bands of muscle)
7. Descending colon
8. Sigmoid colon
9. Rectum
10. Anus
11. Anal canal
12. Internal anal sphincter (involuntary)
13. External anal sphincter (voluntary)

©Hayden-McNeil, LLC

Figure 4.6. Large Intestine

Liver

The **liver** is the largest gland in the body. It assists with digestion by producing and secreting bile. It is located in the upper right quadrant of the abdomen beneath the diaphragm. Entering the bottom of the liver is the hepatic portal vein, covered in the last unit, and exiting the top of the liver are the hepatic veins that empty into the inferior vena cava. Bile is produced in the lobules of the liver and leaves the liver by way of the hepatic ducts. On the inferior surface of the liver the **right hepatic duct**, which drains the right lobe, and the **left hepatic duct**, which drains the left lobe unite to form the **common hepatic duct**. The hepatic duct unites with the **cystic duct** leaving the gallbladder to form the **common bile duct**.

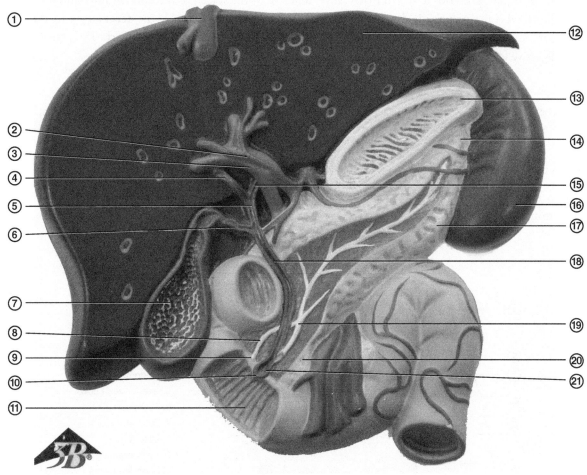

Liver with Gall Bladder, Pancreas and Duodenum LT-VE315, 3B Scientific®

1. Inferior vena cava	8. Accessory pancreatic duct	15. Left hepatic duct
2. Hepatic artery	9. Minor duodenal papilla	16. Spleen
3. Hepatic portal vein	10. Major duodenal papilla	17. Pancreas (body)
4. Right hepatic duct	11. Duodenum	18. Common bile duct
5. Common hepatic duct	12. Liver	19. Pancreatic duct
6. Cystic duct	13. Stomach	20. Head of pancreas
7. Gallbladder	14. Tail of pancreas	21. Hepatopancreatic ampulla (Ampulla of Vater)

Figure 4.7. Liver, Gallbladder, and Pancreas

Gallbladder

The **gallbladder** is a pear-shaped sac located on the inferior of the liver. It is a storage sac for bile. The bile leaves the gallbladder through the **cystic duct**. The cystic duct joins the common hepatic duct as mentioned earlier to form the **common bile duct**. The common bile duct carries bile to the duodenum. The common bile duct joins the **pancreatic duct** and enters the duodenum together. This can present a problem since the pancreatic duct can possibly be blocked by a gallstone that becomes lodged at the juncture of the common bile duct and the pancreatic duct. This can lead to acute pancreatitis.

Pancreas

The pancreas is located posterior to the stomach and extends from the spleen to the duodenum. Running down the center of the gland is the **pancreatic duct** and usually has a branch off it known as the **accessory pancreatic duct**. The pancreatic duct empties into the duodenum inferiorly to the accessory pancreatic duct. The pancreatic ducts carry the digestive enzymes and bicarbonate ion synthesized by the pancreas to the duodenum.

PART 2

URINARY SYSTEM

The urinary system consists of the kidney, ureters, urinary bladder, and urethra. The functional unit of the kidney is the nephron.

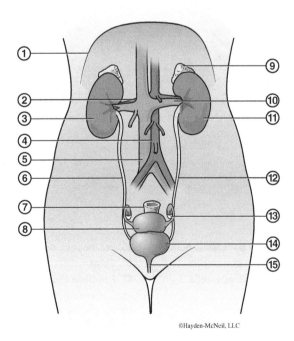

1. Diaphragm
2. Right renal artery
3. Right kidney
4. Abdominal aorta
5. Inferior vena cava
6. Right ureter
7. Rectum
8. Uterus
9. Left adrenal gland
10. Left renal vein
11. Left kidney
12. Left ureter
13. Left ovary
14. Urinary bladder
15. Urethra

©Hayden-McNeil, LLC

Figure 4.8. Urinary System

Kidneys

The kidneys remove waste products from the blood, form urine, and help regulate fluid and electrolytes as well as assist in acid–base balance. They are located on either side of the vertebral column on the posterior abdominal wall in the retroperitoneal space.

The kidney is a bean-shaped organ that is surrounded by a reddish brown fibrous **renal capsule**. Internally the renal tissue is composed of the cortex and the medulla. The **cortex** is the outer region, however in the kidney some cortex tissue is found between the medullary tissues. These regions of cortex are the **renal columns**.

The **medulla** regions are shaped like pyramids and as a result are called **renal pyramids**. The tips of the pyramids are the **papillae** (singular papilla). This is where the urine leaves the nephrons. The urine is collected in the **calyces** (singular **calyx**) which are cup-like structures situated over the papillae. A **minor calyx** collects urine from only one renal papilla. Several minor calyces merge to form one major calyx. A **major calyx** (KAY-liks) (plural: calyces (KAY-lah-seez) collects urine from several minor calyces. The major calyces merge to form the **renal pelvis**. This is a funnel-shaped structure that is large at the top and narrows at the bottom to form the ureter.

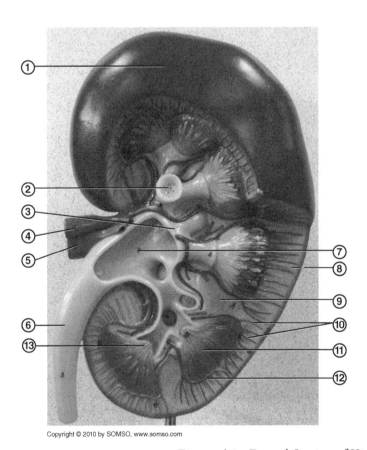

1. Renal capsule
2. Minor calyx
3. Major calyx
4. Renal artery
5. Renal vein
6. Ureter
7. Renal pelvis
8. Renal cortex
9. Renal column
10. Interlobular artery
11. Renal pyramid (medulla)
12. Arcuate artery
13. Papilla

Copyright © 2010 by SOMSO, www.somso.com

Figure 4.9. Frontal Section of Kidney

Ureters

The **ureters** (u-REE-ter) are muscular tubes that extend from the renal pelvis to the urinary bladder. They act as a duct to carry the urine formed in the kidneys to the urinary bladder. Urine is moved through the ureters by peristaltic waves.

Urinary Bladder

The **urinary bladder** is a hollow, distensible smooth muscle organ that serves as a reservoir for urine before it is excreted from the body. It is located in the pelvic cavity posterior to the pubic symphysis and the pubic bone.

The ureters enter through the posterior wall of the bladder in the region known as the **trigone**. The inferior narrowing area of the bladder is the neck of the bladder. This is where the urethra exits the bladder.

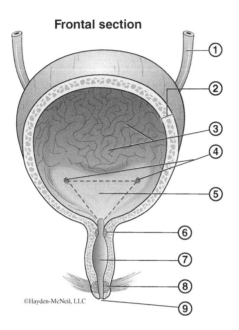

Frontal section

1. Ureter
2. Detrusor muscle
3. Rugae
4. Ureteral openings
5. Trigone
6. Internal urethral sphincter
7. Urethra
8. External urethral sphincter
9. External urethral orifice

©Hayden-McNeil, LLC

Figure 4.10. Bladder

Urethra

The **urethra** (u-REE-thrah) carries the urine from the bladder out of the body. The urethra in the female is very short and only serves as part of the urinary system. In the male the urethra is much longer and serves as part of both the urinary system and the male reproductive system. There are two sphincters controlling the movement of urine through the urethra. The internal urethral sphincter is smooth muscle and involuntary. The external urethral sphincter is skeletal muscle and under voluntary control.

Blood Flow through the Nephron

Blood enters the kidney through the **renal artery**. Once the renal artery enters the kidney it divides many times as it approaches the nephron. As the arteries branch at the base of the pyramids it becomes the **arcuate artery** (ARE-kyah-what). This is a branch of the **interlobar artery**. Branching off the arcuate artery is the **interlobular artery** that carries the blood toward the nephron. Branching off the interlobular artery is the **afferent arteriole** which carries the blood to be filtered into the glomerulus. The glomerulus is a specialized capillary bed that functions to filter the blood passing through it. After the blood is filtered it leaves the glomerulus by way of the **efferent arteriole**. The efferent arteriole is smaller in diameter than the afferent arteriole. The efferent arterioles lead into the **peritubular capillaries**. These capillary beds travel along with the tubules of the nephrons and take part in reabsorption and secretion as well as nourishing the nephron. The peritubular capillaries flow into venules that drain into the **interlobular veins**. The venous blood eventually makes its way to the **renal vein** which drains into the inferior vena cava.

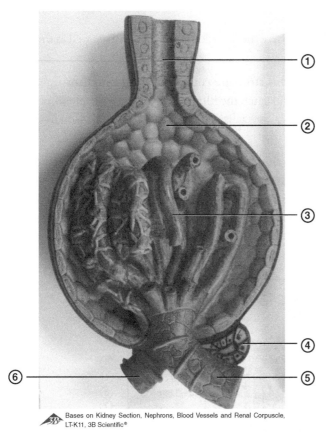

1. Proximal convoluted tubule
2. Glomerular (Bowman's) capsule
3. Glomerulus
4. Distal convoluted tubule
5. Afferent arteriole
6. Efferent arteriole

Bases on Kidney Section, Nephrons, Blood Vessels and Renal Corpuscle, LT-K11, 3B Scientific®

Figure 4.11. Glomerulus and Glomerular Capsule

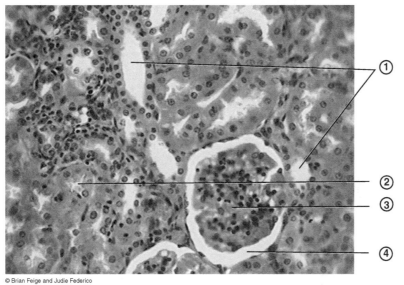

1. Distal convoluted tubules
2. Proximal convoluted tubule
3. Glomerulus
4. Glomerular capsule

© Brian Feige and Judie Federico

Figure 4.12. Renal Cortex 400×

Nephron

The **nephron** is the functional unit of the kidney. This is where the filtration of blood occurs as well as the reabsorption and secretion that occurs in the formation of urine.

The beginning of the nephron is the **renal corpuscle**. This structure consists of the **glomerulus** (glo-MER-u-lus) and the **Bowman's capsule** or **glomerular capsule** that will catch the filtrate formed from the blood passing through the glomerulus. As mentioned earlier the glomerulus is a specialized capillary bed. The Bowman's capsule is the beginning of the tubular structure of the nephron.

The filtrate leaves the Bowman's capsule and enters the **proximal convoluted tubule**. The majority of the reabsorption occurs here. The filtrate then flows into the **nephron loop (of Henle)**. First, it travels down the **descending limb**, around the bottom of the loop and into the **ascending limb**. The next tubule is the **distal convoluted tubule**. Secretion may occur here as well as in the **collecting duct**. The urine leaves the distal convoluted tubule and enters the collecting duct. Many nephrons empty into the same collecting duct. The collecting duct will carry the urine out of the nephron through the papillae of the pyramids into the calyces.

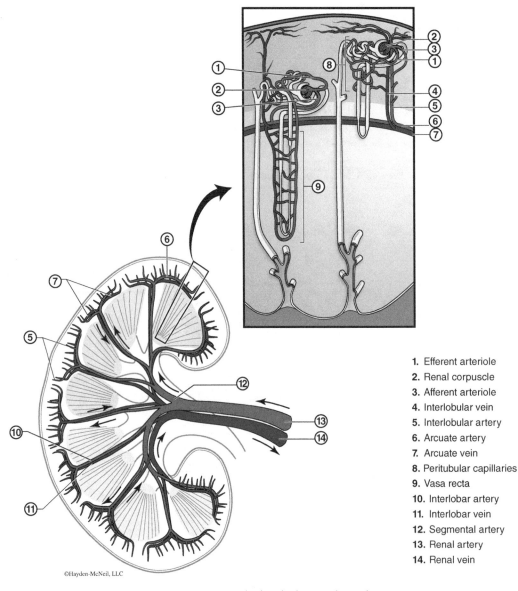

1. Efferent arteriole
2. Renal corpuscle
3. Afferent arteriole
4. Interlobular vein
5. Interlobular artery
6. Arcuate artery
7. Arcuate vein
8. Peritubular capillaries
9. Vasa recta
10. Interlobar artery
11. Interlobar vein
12. Segmental artery
13. Renal artery
14. Renal vein

©Hayden-McNeil, LLC

Figure 4.13. Renal Blood Flow and Nephron

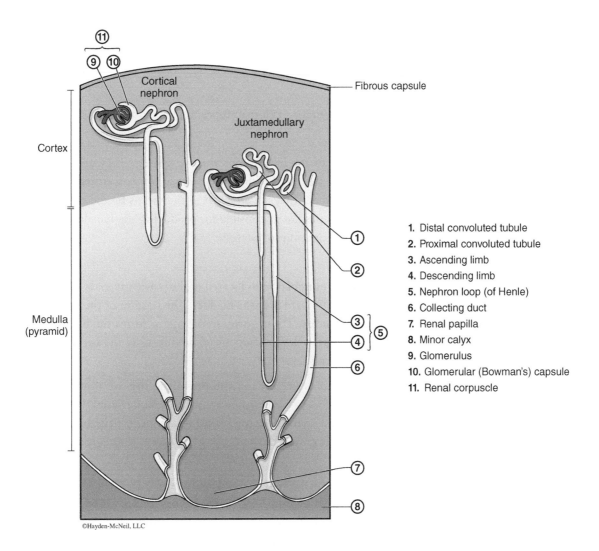

1. Distal convoluted tubule
2. Proximal convoluted tubule
3. Ascending limb
4. Descending limb
5. Nephron loop (of Henle)
6. Collecting duct
7. Renal papilla
8. Minor calyx
9. Glomerulus
10. Glomerular (Bowman's) capsule
11. Renal corpuscle

©Hayden-McNeil, LLC

Figure 4.14. Cortical and Juxtamedullary Nephrons

PART 3

FEMALE REPRODUCTIVE SYSTEM

The female reproductive system includes the ovaries, uterus, fallopian tubes, vagina, and the external genitalia.

Ovaries

The **ovaries** are the gonads or reproductive organs of the female reproductive system. They are oval shaped and measure about 3.5 cm in length, 2 cm in width, and 1 cm in thickness. They are located on either side of the uterus just below the opening of the fallopian or uterine tubes. They are attached to the uterus by the **ovarian ligaments** and are also attached to the broad ligament. The ovaries are responsible for producing the female gametes, the egg or ovum, as well as the female sex hormones: estrogens and progesterone.

Uterus

The **uterus** is a hollow pear-shaped organ with thick muscular walls located in the pelvic cavity. It is located between the urinary bladder and the rectum. It usually flexes forward over the bladder. The portion of the uterus superior to the entrance of the uterine tubes is known as the **fundus**. The majority of the uterus forms the **body** of the uterus, located between the fundus and the cervix. The narrow lower segment of the uterus is the **cervix**. This segment projects into the vagina.

The uterus is held in place by eight ligaments, four of which are the two broad and the two round ligaments. The **broad ligament** is a fold of the peritoneum that attaches to the uterus, uterine tubes, and ovaries. It extends from the uterus to the pelvic walls and floor. Within the broad ligament is the **round ligament**, which attaches the superior portion of the uterus and extends to the anterior pelvic wall. By connecting the uterus to the pelvic wall it helps to stabilize or maintain the position of the uterus.

The wall of the uterus has three layers. The innermost layer is the **endometrium** (EN-DOEMEE-tree-um). The superior portion of this layer is shed during menses. The middle layer is the **myometrium** (MI-OMEE-tree-um), a very thick smooth muscular layer that is responsible for uterine contractions. The outer layer, which is not complete, is made up of the peritoneum and is known as the perimetrium. It does not completely cover the cervix.

Uterine/Fallopian Tubes

The **uterine** or **fallopian tubes** extend from ovaries to the uterus. They open near the ovaries and enter the uterus in the upper region of the body, just below the fundus of the uterus. It serves as a channel for the transport of the ovum from the ovary to the uterus. It is also the site of fertilization.

The narrowest portion of the uterine tube that is located adjacent to the uterus is the **isthmus** (IS-mahs). The widest and longest portion of the uterine tube is the **ampulla**. It extends from the isthmus to the infundibulum. The uterine tubes expand near the ovaries into the **infundibulum** (IN-fund-DIB-u-lum). At the end of the infundibulum are finger-like projections called the **fimbriae** (FIM-bre). Beating of the fimbrae directs the ovum to the opening of the uterine tube. Peristaltic contractions and ciliary action moves the ovum towards the uterus.

Vagina

The **vagina** is a hollow muscular tube that extends from the cervix to the exterior of the body. It surrounds the cervix of the uterus and is located between the bladder and the rectum. The vagina serves as a receptacle for the semen, an exit route for the endometrial tissue during menstruation, and the lower part of the birth canal.

Vulva

The **vulva** is the female external genitalia. It includes the labia majora, the labia minora, and the clitoris. The **labia majora** (singular, labium) are skin covered rounded folds of adipose tissue that protect the external genitalia. The **labia minora** are flat folds of tissue inside the labia majora. They surround the urethral and vaginal orifices. Anteriorly they merge to form the prepuce of the clitoris. The **clitoris** (KLIT-o-ris) is a small projection inside the labia minora in the anterior vulva. It is erectile tissue that becomes engorged with blood when stimulated.

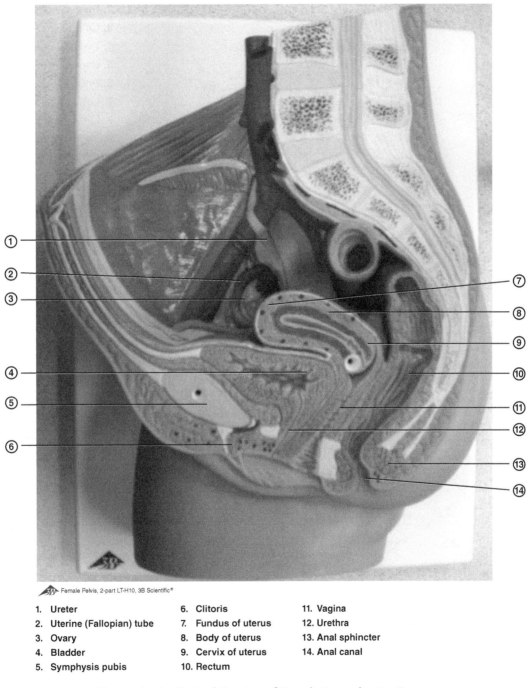

Female Pelvis, 2-part LT-H10, 3B Scientific®

1. Ureter	6. Clitoris	11. Vagina
2. Uterine (Fallopian) tube	7. Fundus of uterus	12. Urethra
3. Ovary	8. Body of uterus	13. Anal sphincter
4. Bladder	9. Cervix of uterus	14. Anal canal
5. Symphysis pubis	10. Rectum	

Figure 4.15. Sagittal Section of Female Reproductive System

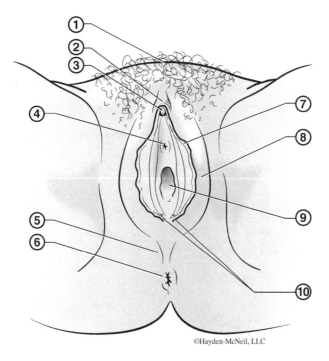

1. Mons pubis
2. Prepuce of clitoris
3. Clitoris
4. Urethral orifice
5. Perineum
6. Anus
7. Labium minora
8. Labium majora
9. Vaginal orifice
10. Bartholin's glands

©Hayden-McNeil, LLC

Figure 4.16. Vulva

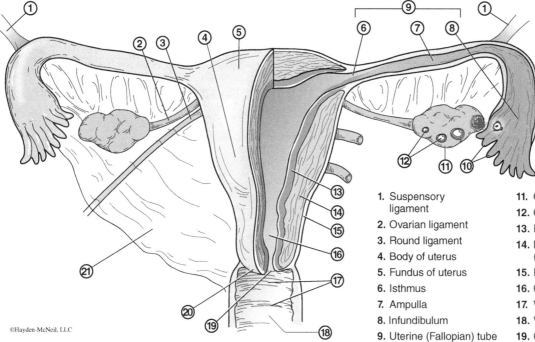

1. Suspensory ligament
2. Ovarian ligament
3. Round ligament
4. Body of uterus
5. Fundus of uterus
6. Isthmus
7. Ampulla
8. Infundibulum
9. Uterine (Fallopian) tube
10. Fimbriae

11. Ovary
12. Ovarian follicles
13. Endometrium
14. Myometrium (smooth muscle)
15. Perimetrium
16. Cervical canal
17. Vaginal rugae
18. Vagina
19. Cervical os
20. Cervix
21. Broad ligament

©Hayden-McNeil, LLC

Figure 4.17. Frontal View of Female Reproductive System

Part 4

Male Reproductive System

The male reproductive system consists of the gonads, the testes. There is also a series of ducts that carry the sperm: the epididymis, vas deferens, ejaculatory duct, and urethra. In addition to the gonad and ducts there are the glands that produce seminal fluid: the seminal vesicles, prostate, and bulbourethal/Cowper's glands. The support structures include the penis, the spermatic cord, and the scrotum.

Testes

The **testes** (TES-tez) (singular, **testis** (TES-tis)) are the organs responsible for producing both the sperm and testosterone. They are located outside the body in the **scrotum**. The scrotum is a skin covered pouch that contains blood vessels, muscles, and nerves in addition to the testis. The testes are located outside the body because the temperature needs to be 3–5 degrees below body temperature to properly produce sperm.

The testes are divided into lobules that contain the **seminiferous tubules** (SEM-INIF-ahrus). The sperm are produced in these tubules. The interstitial cells between the seminiferous tubules produce testosterone. This hormone is responsible for the secondary sex characteristics in males.

Epididymis

Epididymis (EP-IDID-imis), (plural, epididymides) is a long, tightly coiled tube that exits the top of each testis, descends posteriorly and then ascends to become the vas deferens. The epididymis is located in the scrotum with the testis. This duct stores the sperm produced in the testis until maturity and transports the sperm to the vas deferens which is continuous with the epididymis.

There are three regions of the epididymis: the head, the body, and the tail. The tail is not as tightly coiled as the rest of the epididymis and becomes the vas deferens.

Vas Deferens

The **vas deferens** (DEF-er-ENS) (plural, vasa deferentia) is also known as the ductus deferens. It continues from the epididymis and carries the sperm away from the testis. The vas deferens passes through the spermatic cord into the pelvic cavity behind the bladder and merges with the seminal vesicles.

The vas deferens enlarges as it unites with the duct of the seminal vesicle; this is the **ampulla of the vas deferens**. The **common ejaculatory duct** is formed by the union of the ampulla of the vas deferens and the seminal vesicle duct. This duct passes through the prostate gland and empties into the urethra. The **urethra** will carry the sperm and the seminal fluid, now known as semen out of the body.

Spermatic Cord

The connective tissue structure that creates a passageway for structures to pass between the abdominal cavity and the scrotum is the **spermatic cord**. It contains the vas deferens, arteries, veins, lymphatics, nerves as well as the cremaster muscle. It begins in the abdominal cavity, passes through the inguinal canal, and enters the scrotum to reach the testis.

Seminal Vesicles

The **seminal vesicles** (SEM-inahl) are two convoluted sac-like glands located on the posterior surface of the urinary bladder near the base. These glands produce a seminal fluid that contains alkaline fluid, fructose, and prostaglandins. This fluid is added to the sperm in the vas deferens and moves into the ejaculatory duct.

Prostate Gland

The **prostate gland** is a singular gland that surrounds the urethra just below the bladder. It produces alkaline seminal fluid that is added to the sperm and seminal fluid already present. It is about the size of a walnut and is located near the rectum which allows a physician to palpate the gland during a physical exam. The portion of the urethra that passes through this gland is called the **prostatic urethra**. The portion of the urethra between the prostate gland and the penis is the **membranous urethra**.

Bulbourethral Glands

The **bulbourethral** (BUL-bo-u-REE-thral) or **Cowper's glands** are two small glands located inferiorly to the prostate and posterior to the urethra. These glands also produce seminal fluid. The main component they add is mucus which helps lubricate the end of the penis.

Penis

The **penis** is the external sex organ of the male. It contains three columns of erectile tissue. In the posterior penis there are two columns of tissue known as the **corpora cavernosa** (KORE-pour-ah KAV-ahr-nosa) (singular: corpus). Extending through the center of each of these cylinders of erectile tissue are arteries that dilate during erection. In the anterior penis is a singular column known as the **corpus spongiosum** (KORE-pus SPON-jee-O-sum). In the center of the cylinder is the urethra. This portion of the urethra is known as the **penile urethra**.

At the distal end of the penis the corpus spongiosum extends over the ends of the corpora cavernosa to form the tip known as the **glans penis**. This contains the external urethral orifice. The glans is covered by a loose fold of skin called the **prepuce** (PRE-pyoos) or foreskin. This is the tissue that is removed during a circumcision.

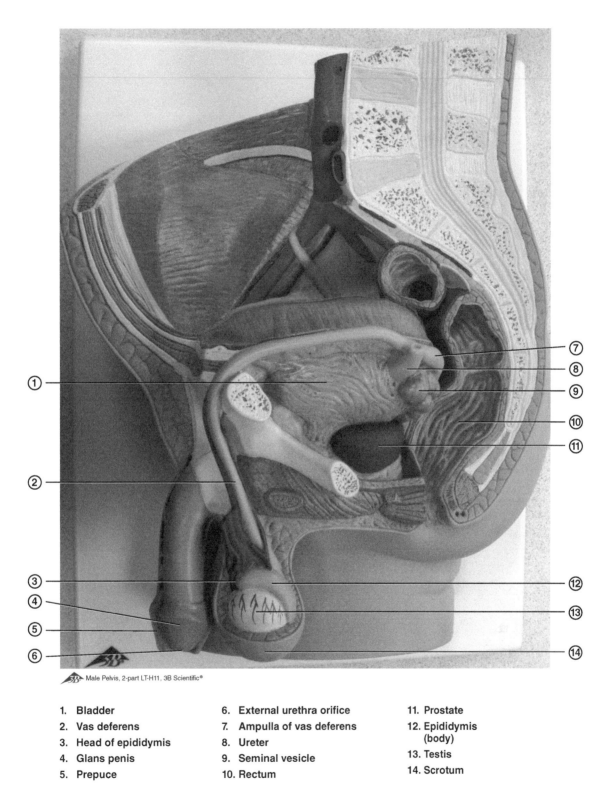

Male Pelvis, 2-part LT-H11, 3B Scientific®

1. Bladder
2. Vas deferens
3. Head of epididymis
4. Glans penis
5. Prepuce
6. External urethra orifice
7. Ampulla of vas deferens
8. Ureter
9. Seminal vesicle
10. Rectum
11. Prostate
12. Epididymis (body)
13. Testis
14. Scrotum

Figure 4.18. Sagittal View Male Reproductive System

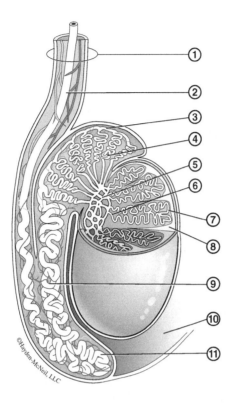

1. Spermatic cord
2. Vas deferens
3. Head of epididymis
4. Efferent ductules
5. Rete testis
6. Straight tubule
7. Seminiferous tubule
8. Tunica albuginea
9. Body of epididymis
10. Scrotal cavity
11. Tail of epididymis

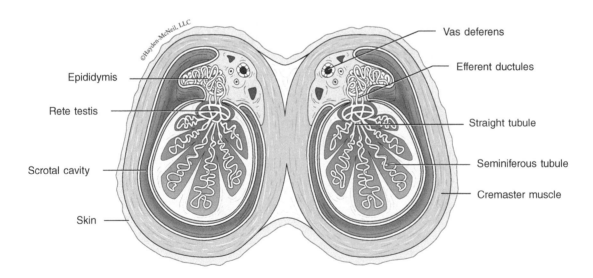

Figure 4.19. Frontal View of Testes and Epididymis

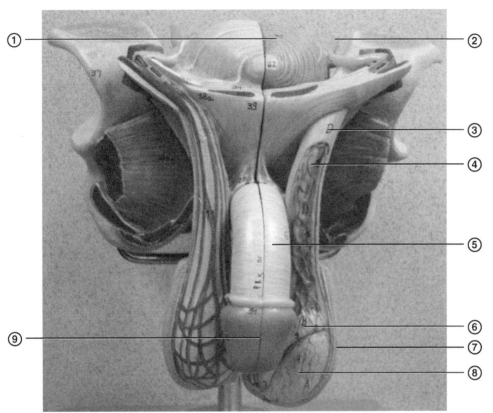

1. Bladder
2. Ureter
3. Spermatic cord
4. Vas deferens
5. Penis
6. Epididymis
7. Scrotum
8. Testis
9. Glans penis

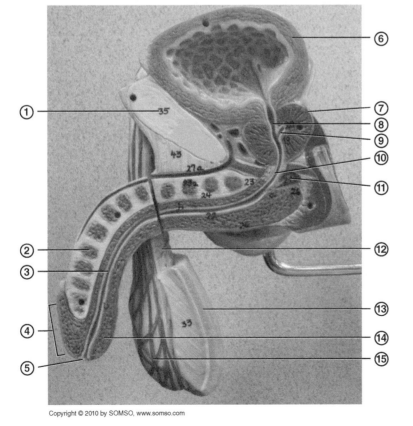

1. Symphysis pubis
2. Corpus cavernosa
3. Penile urethra
4. Glans penis
5. External urethral opening
6. Bladder
7. Prostate gland
8. Prostatic urethra
9. Common ejaculatory duct
10. Spongy urethra
11. Bulbourethral gland
12. Spermatic cord
13. Scrotum
14. Corpus spongiosum
15. Testis

Figure 4.20. Male Reproductive System

UNIT 4